THE
ROOTS
OF
SCIENCE

An Investigative Journey
Through the World's Religions

HAROLD TURNER

The
DeepSight
Trust

A New Zealand Initiative for Religion and Cultures

ISBN 0-9582012-2-6
First published 1998
The DeepSight Trust
PO Box 87-362, Meadowbank
Auckland, New Zealand.

Typeset in Berkeley and Frutiger.
Design and artwork by Streamline Creative Ltd, Auckland.
Cover design by C. Humberstone

Printed by Colorcraft Ltd, Hong Kong.

Dedicated to the Memory of Lesslie Newbigin, 1909-1998
Who dared to ignore St Augustine's denial of life
at the Antipodes and warmly supported
the Mission to Our Culture
'Down Under'.

Contents

Contents

Matter Without Depreciation. De-sacralized Time Becomes Historical.
De-sacralized Space and Place. De-sacralizing Society and Persons.
The Hebrew Revolution in History.

TRIBAL AND JUDAEO-CHRISTIAN COSMOLOGY AFFINITY:
Deep-Rooted Affinity With the Duality Model.
Tribal Peoples Enter the World of Science.

Foreword

As the 20th century merges into the 21st, science and religion appear to be losing popular support. There is a perception that there is no connection, indeed even a natural conflict, between science and theology, and that the rise of the high technology, science-based, modern society has contributed to the moral and ethical malaise of our times. In such times, the emergence of a study that explores and locates the origin and development of the scientific method in the faiths of the world can only be of value.

There always has been a coherent relationship between a people's belief systems and their attitude to science and technology. Cultural attitudes, based on theology, have and still do determine the acceptable methodology of intellectual inquiry, the acquisition of knowledge through observation and experimentation, and the status of science in society.

A growing number of worldwide phenomena are appearing which are covertly and often overtly anti-science. Examples of these include: the emergence of creationism and the demand that it be given equal status to the evolutionary theories; the raising of indigenous knowledge and belief systems to the status of a science; an emphasis in education on using the constructivist approach in which culture and experience are valued rather than logic and analysis. Ideological fervour rather than logical argument based on empirically determined and internally consistent data underlie their growth.

Many people (including some scientists) are unaware of the philosophical and historical basis of the scientific deductive and experimental methodology, and how closely the evolution and direction of intellectual enquiry and technology have been influenced by theology.

The peoples of ancient civilizations, with their worship of complex arrays of gods and spirits, many of which represent the forces of nature, tended to be keen observers of the natural world (and particularly of astronomy) but used their observations only for ritual and religious purposes. The deductive method and thus science could only take root and flourish when the contemporary theology allowed a rational world.

In this context it is instructive to consider one of the world's great civilizations, that of the Roman Empire. This emphasised obedience to strong family and social values defined by a rigid legal framework, and had an animistic belief system in which spirits governed all aspects of life. While the legacies of Roman civilizations are substantial – Roman law forms the basis of most of the western world's legal systems and Roman engineering works remain the marvel of the modern world – the intellectual contribution of the Romans to science is negligible. None of the scientists and philosophers who were participants in the debates, discoveries and advances of the 16th and 17th centuries, during the so-called scientific revolution, none would have had any doubt that there was a strong inter-dependence between the contemporary theological debates that led ultimately to the Reformation and the emergence of the deductive (scientific) method. They drew on ideas that natural phenomena could be dealt with in abstract (mathematical) terms and that knowledge was systematic and could be based on empirical observations. These ideas originated with the early Greek and Islamic thinkers, and were integrated with the concept, defined by Christian theology, of an ordered world that did not require any mythical or magical explanation.

Paradoxically, although the convergence of these concepts made the development of so-called Western science possible, the postulate of one of the great thinkers of the period, Galileo, that the (mathematical) laws that controlled nature were immutable and inexorable and independent of the authority of the Scriptures, provided the first major divergence between science and religion.

Foreword

Not all science can be described mathematically, although all can be described rationally. The belief that nature is rational resulted in observation and experimentally-based modes of enquiry which in turn led to interpretations of patterns of behaviour and the development of models which can be tested and modified. This concept of open intellectual debate, iterative rigorous testing of ideas against empirical data and consequent modification of models, that is the scientific method, has expanded beyond the scientific community and also underpins modern democratic society.

Probably the most important intellectual contribution that science has made to contemporary thought is that the relationship between mankind and nature is not predetermined and immutable – it can be investigated, understood and modified. The future can be better than the past. This book explores and elucidates the origins and rise of science in a theological context. The challenge for both science and theology is to achieve a partnership in which the issues of modern society can be addressed and which does indeed lead to a better future.

Philippa Black
Professor of Geology, University of Auckland
Immediate Past President, The Royal Society of New Zealand
September 1998

Preface

This essay is one of the first in the publications series of The DeepSight Trust, which is described as 'A New Zealand Initiative for Religion and Cultures'. This Trust absorbs and continues the work begun by the earlier Gospel and Cultures Trust, and so traces back to the Gospel and Culture Movement in Britain from the early 1980s. It may not be immediately clear what a book under the present title has to do with the cultural concerns of these bodies.

While it can stand alone under its title, it is also presented as a case study of what may well be regarded as one of the core features of Western culture, its science; this not only shapes Western culture but increasingly impinges upon and is adopted by almost every other culture in the world.

While Western society may appear secularized – an assumption I shall question in this text – most of these other cultures have a religion at their core. If science is to be accepted by them, then its relation to their various religious traditions becomes critically important, and must be examined at the most fundamental level possible. This I endeavour to do through their various worldviews, and especially through what I shall explain as their cosmologies, their ultimate axioms about the universe we live in.

In this enquiry we shall find that the history of the essential idea and axioms of science by its very nature leads us through the religions of the tribal cultures and the Asian peoples to the insignificant, Hebrew tribes of Semites, who migrated out of Mesopotamia some three millennia ago. We shall therefore be surveying the root axioms or worldviews of these three groups, the Tribal, the Asian and the Semitic, in relation to those necessary for the development of theoretical science.

The cosmological aspect with which I am concerned has little to do with astrophysics or the history of the natural world since the Big Bang or whatever; this kind of cosmology belongs to the natural sciences and changes with the advance of science. Rather am I dealing with a more philosophic and theological aspect of cosmology, the view of the relations between nature, humanity and the divine, regarded as three 'levels' of the universe or cosmos. These views have great historical stability, are rooted in one or other of the major religious traditions, and are found in all cultures.

Religions themselves do not usually articulate their cosmologies in any formal or explicit way, but their adherents all have operative views expressed in their behaviour and within what Michael Polanyi has taught us to call the tacit dimension of our knowledge. Our first task, therefore, is to identify the main types of cosmology and then to critique these in their relation to the basic requirements for the development of science. We may expect some cosmologies to be more congenial to science than others, and so it proves when we examine the distinctive cosmology of the Hebrew people.

This conclusion will surprise, annoy, even anger many who have absorbed current stereotypes about religion and science, or it may please others rather too readily, without any depth of understanding. The essay, however, presents the basic religious worldviews on the one hand, and on the other the history of science as it has developed its basic axioms, either hindered or helped by the cosmologies of various times and places.

By this I mean not a history of the particular achievements of science but rather a history of what makes science possible and can sustain it amid the cultural confusions of our time. Neither the general public nor many working scientists may be aware of the serious attacks upon science from the postmodern forces in Western culture. These would reduce science to a series of temporary belief systems created within each culture for its own immediate needs, without any inherent relation to the truth of how things really are for all peoples, cultures and times. If this 'deconstructive' view presented in chapters 10 and 11 alarms some, then I trust that my 'reconstruction' in chapter 12 will renew their trust in a future for science as we have come to know it since the 16th century.

Our enquiry also speaks to what Samuel Huntingdon is teaching us to see as *The Clash of Civilizations and the Remaking of World Order*, where each civilization or major culture-group has its own religious basis in a multi-cultural world.[1] Without the basic examination here proposed, most of the current enthusiasm for indigenous cultures and multi-cultural relations is dangerously superficial or misguided. It is hoped that this work will contribute to remedying these crippling defects.

To those who have followed the increasing literature in this field, much in these pages will be familiar, except perhaps for the attention I have given the tribal peoples in chapter 2. This grew out of including the tribal religions in the neglected subject of the phenomenology of religion, because of their historical importance as 'our basic, common religious heritage'. An example of the continuing neglect of tribal religion in prestigious quarters is found in chapter 3, note 2.

There is other related new material in the 'unexpected' chapter 9 on new religious movements in tribal societies. These have provided a major research and publication field ever since I stumbled into one such movement in West Africa in 1957, and went on to identify similar developments in tribal cultures in all continents from the time of Columbus. They are included in this historical survey because they provide an excellent test case for the basic thesis of these pages.

The only other section that will probably be new to many is my chapter 5 on John Philoponus as "the greatest theoretical physicist of classical antiquity", and the most neglected of the early Church Fathers, at least insofar as science is concerned. In spite of the key position he holds in these matters, there was his disappearance from the European world of thought for a thousand years, his first rediscovery late in the mediaeval period, then his second disappearance and gradual rediscovery from the 1950s – note 14 in chapter 5 provides an outline of the latter. I hope that others will share in the pleasure and value of my own discovery of Philoponus.

It remains to explain that this essay first took shape for a one-day Saturday seminar in February 1996, as part of the programme of the University of Auckland's Centre For Continuing Education. Without the incentive and stimulus of that occasion and its excellent facilities I doubt if I would have put this material together in this more developed form. Certain matters critical of the Centre and illustrative of my thesis were too clear and within my direct experience to be ignored; these critiques in no way diminish my gratitude for the opportunity the Centre provided, and also to those who endured the six hours of the original oral form.

I must also acknowledge a longer standing incentive provided by invitations to try out some of these sections in Dr. Stephen May's courses on science and theology at St. John's Theological College. The College library and its helpful staff have also made an essential contribution.

Specialists will want to qualify some of my broad generalizations or my over-simplifying of complex issues. I am aware of this but also of how easy it is 'not to see the wood for the trees'; my concern is with those who have never been presented with the overall story – with the main religious world-views, the roots of science, and their inter-relationships. This is therefore more of a popular than a specialist study, but at the same time I believe it has something fresh to say on some fundamental issues.

Harold Turner
Auckland
September 1998

Notes
1 Date references have been changed to the current CE (Common Era) from old AD and to BCE (Before the Common Era) from the old BC.
2. Abbreviations:
    c. = century; ca. = about; b. = born; d. = died; f. = following page; ff. = following pages; fl. = flourished (i.e., main period)

CHAPTER ONE

Introduction

In this book we shall be travelling, in our minds, over a route that took some of our ancestors 3000 years or more to traverse. During these three millennia what the world knows as science was born and has grown to the astonishing stature it has today. In the same three millennia all the present major religious faiths appeared, and have spread to their present constituencies. We shall be examining the historical relations between the development of science and the worldviews of these religions, and the integral relation between science and one of these worldviews.

History at a Discount
In doing so we are in the ironical position of knowing more about the history of ourselves and of all other cultures than any previous generation, and at the same time being less interested in history than ever before. For modern and especially postmodern Western societies, tradition, institutions and the authority that goes with them are at a discount. "To live for the moment is the prevailing passion – to live for oneself, not for your predecessors or posterity. We are fast losing the sense of historical continuity, the sense of belonging to a succession of generations originating in the past and stretching into the future."[1] Therefore, as an historian laments, "the deep question of our age is whether or not history matters. In the typical contemporary

culture...there is little sense that an appeal to historical precedent or principle would in fact settle anything. Presentism is the fad of our age. Only the modern or new affects us. The past seems far away."[2] Even well-educated and highly professional people show a sad ignorance of or indifference to history.

This is especially serious when scientists in such a scientific culture are uninformed about the history of science. True, a medical man may know a good deal about the history of a particular disease in which he is interested, or a botanist about the history of plant classification. Yet both may have no conception whatsoever about the origins of science as such, of its basic principles and where these have come from; or worse still they may depend on one of the popular stereotypes of these matters.

It might be thought that the notable development since the mid-20th century of university departments for the history of science would remedy this. It appears that these are now in danger of being cut back or of being re-absorbed into their departments of origin, as a luxury that cash-strapped universities can no longer afford. In any case they seldom met the need for the deep analysis of the cultural origins of science and for the comprehensive overview that is being attempted here. History of particular scientists or of specific developments might be excellent, except that they suffered from seeing the trees of the forest in their individuality without understanding of the forest itself, of seeing the part but not the whole. When the whole consists of a worldview or a cosmology based on a religion, then the history of science has often been conspicuously inadequate.

Alternative Attitudes

In view of this inadequacy and of the great variety of attitudes about the relations between science and religion that do exist, it will be useful to take a quick look at these. They lie not only on the surface of our society, and are expressed in the media and often conveyed in our public education systems, but they also lie embedded in the minds both of scientists and of religious believers. We can classify these broadly as follows:

1. *The conflict model:* Science studies this world and alone controls truth. Religion is essentially in opposition, with its other-worldliness and myths. Two famous books late in the 19th century expressed it well: J.W. Draper's *History of the Conflict Between Science and Religion* (London, 1875) and A.D.

White's *A History of the Warfare of Science with Theology in Christendom* (New York, 1896).

Although their scholarship is now thoroughly discredited by the new 20th century discipline of the history of science, these views persist. They even emerged in an article in the high-level journal *Science & Education*. It was entitled 'Is Religious Education Compatible with Science Education?' It came from a biologist-philosopher and a physicist-philosopher at McGill, a major university, and the answer was a resounding "No!" – religious education is actually an impediment and should be eradicated at all levels. I have been privileged to be one of the respondents to this blunt claim, in the issue which is devoted to this theme, and I have included some of the ground we shall cover here.[3]

2. *The conflict model reversed*: The religion revealed in the Christian scriptures has the literal truth about the whole of creation, and the evidence of science has to be reinterpreted to fit in. Most current science teaching is simply not true. This is the view among some earnest Christians, supporting 'Creation Science', since it sees the creation of the universe as a recent event within the short biblical time span suggested by the book of Genesis (so it is thought) and the subsequent genealogies. This view deserves to be as discredited as the one above by responsible scholarship in both science and theology.

3. *The complementary model*, where science and religion are seen as two different kinds of truth, answering two different sorts of questions, from two different perspectives which cannot clash. Science asks the factual questions of What? and How? Religion asks the purpose or value questions of Why? or What for? This leaves us with a split between two kinds of truth, that never meet. Life, of course, doesn't work in this divided fashion and people ask about the purpose or value of scientific knowledge, or else reduce religious knowledge to merely subjective opinion with no basis in fact or reality. Both these attitudes are at work in contemporary culture, and offer a false peace between the two approaches. Lesslie Newbigin has put it well:

> The same person can be a scientist or a believer, depending whether he
> is in his laboratory or in church...It is true that we sometimes see (to
> use the famous illustration) a picture of two human profiles as if it were
> a picture of a vase. It is true – in the more famous Indian parable – that
> one can see a piece of rope as if it were a snake. But no sane person is

content to leave matters there...we will not be content until we have decided which it is – rope or a snake. Having discovered what it is, we shall then be able to understand the different ways of seeing it...But we shall not be content until we have reached that point [and so have unified our knowledge].[4]

4. *The temporary, God-of-the-gaps model*: Here science provides an accumulating body of truth and religion merely fills in some of the remaining gaps in our knowledge, with its speculations or substitutes. These may tide us over our temporary ignorance, but this religious knowledge is not grounded in fact, and the gap constantly shrinks or these views are radically corrected as real scientific knowledge advances, and "God has to retreat to another temporary refuge."[5]

5. *The relativity 'there is no truth' model*: this postmodern contemporary position in Western culture takes the subjective opinion view of religious truth and applies it to all knowledge, including even that of science itself. Truth in all areas is either a cultural or a personal construct, or a symbolic statement that serves our own changing needs instead of referring to a factual reality beyond ourselves. So we are wasting our time if we think we are seeking together something really and permanently true about the relations of science and religion in history. Neither has any permanence.

6. *The inter-fertilization model*: this is the model that our discussion in these pages will, I hope, establish – that the truths sought in rather different ways and different areas meet in the end and are congruent with each other. Deep down religion and science need each other, and can fertilize each other, as we seek the whole truth about the whole universe. Ultimately, truth is one, consistent and coherent.

Now we could critique each of these positions in turn, with many complex rebuttals and corrections. We could, for instance, take the first or conflict view and admit that obscurantist religious education with its 'creation science' is an impediment to real science. But then we could equally take presumptuous science education as an impediment to authentic religion. This would refer to 'scientism', the exaggerated belief that science can solve everything. This usually goes with a naturalist philosophy wherein everything is completely determined by natural or physical factors.

Such arguments might serve debating or apologetic purposes, but they would not take us to the heart of the matter, to the rock-bottom relationship between science and religion. This is what I hope to do in a way that you can apply in your further thinking. So often the issues are very simple once we get down to the few basic options. I plan to work with the three world-view options that determine all subsequent beliefs.

The Three Families of Religions

I refer to three options because the world's religions may first be grouped into three broad families, where there is a combination, as in any human family, of family likenesses along with individual differences in its members.

The first group is that of the tribal cultures around the world and deep into the historical past, as well as being still alive and well in many places. I call these the *primal religions,* and I regard them as humanity's common religious heritage, for they lie behind and have left their mark on all the later major religions. In a sense they belong to us all. Their common characteristics will start to appear when we return to the cosmologies they tend to share.

The second family consists of the new religions that arose in Asia in the first millennium BCE and became major faiths extending beyond any one tribe – Zoroastrianism, the Hindu, Buddhist, and Jain faiths in India, and Taoism and Confucianism in China, as well as the religious philosophies of the classical Greek period. I shall later describe these by the term *Axial religions* and set forth their common features.

The third family embraces the three *Semitic faiths* that stem from the Hebrew people and their Semitic cousins – Judaism, Christianity and Islam. Since the race word 'Semitic' in popular usage has become especially associated with the Jews, I shall use the alternative term 'Abrahamic' to refer to this family; it is especially appropriate since all three faiths recognize Abraham in their scriptures as an historical founding father. These three have often been subsumed under the Axial religions and it will be an important task later to show why this classification is wrong and to set forth their distinctive characteristics, and especially those of the Hebrew religion.

There is, however, another classification at a higher level whereby the Axial and the Abrahamic faiths are correctly combined in one category. This two-group classification sees the primal religions as essentially ethno-centric, tied to one *particular* tribe, land and language. By contrast all other religions, that have commonly been called higher, historical, great or world religions, all these may be called *universal* religions. Religions of this kind are universal either in intention (as with Islam and Christianity and increasingly some of the others) or in potential – it is conceivable that they could become widespread religions over many races and regions in a way that is quite inconceivable for any of the primal religions. The latter may borrow from one another but they do not set out to convert one another as the universal religions have done, increasingly do, and conceivably might do.

While we shall operate with the further tripartite distinction it is useful to have made this two-part classification since it supports the distinctiveness of the primal or tribal religions as over against all others. Why we use the three-fold grouping will become more evident as we attend to the differences in worldview or cosmology across the many forms of faith.

The Three Models for Cosmology

The particular section of worldviews that I shall focus on is the view of the whole universe and its contents, and the broad pattern of how these are related to one another. This is cosmology (Greek, 'cosmos', or universe) and in the area that concerns us here there are only three basic options, which correspond to the three families of religion.

Within each of these systems the contents of the cosmos may be classified as the realms of nature, the world of the human, and the sphere of the divine, in a hierarchy that most cultures would recognize. All cultures have their detailed accounts of them, and how they are related, in their own particular cosmology.

Let us visualise a large oval for the cosmos, with three levels for the natural, the human and the divine. I shall call this a *unitary*, closed cosmology, described by the single term 'encapsulated', as it were in a huge egg. This is the characteristic worldview of tribal societies, even in their later sophisticated developments into the great civilizations of the ancient world. We shall examine it more fully, but let us first complete the options with two other forms of cosmology.

The first alternative makes a radical distinction within the cosmos. It separates the spiritual realm of the divine from the material realm of nature – in short it is a *dualist* cosmology. Here human beings stand in various, often ambivalent, positions between the two realms, belonging to each in

The Three Cosmologies

DIAGRAMMATIC SUMMARY

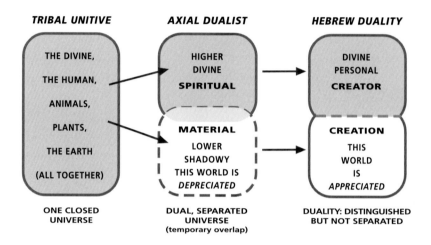

TRIBAL UNITIVE	AXIAL DUALIST	HEBREW DUALITY
THE DIVINE, THE HUMAN, ANIMALS, PLANTS, THE EARTH (ALL TOGETHER)	HIGHER DIVINE SPIRITUAL — MATERIAL LOWER SHADOWY THIS WORLD IS *DEPRECIATED*	DIVINE PERSONAL CREATOR — CREATION THIS WORLD IS *APPRECIATED*
ONE CLOSED UNIVERSE	DUAL, SEPARATED UNIVERSE (temporary overlap)	DUALITY: DISTINGUISHED BUT NOT SEPARATED

different senses. Its dualism is essentially a pluralist view over against the unitary encapsulated view. It emphasizes the many as against a focus on the one, and we shall look into its long history a little later.

The only further option, beyond the unitive and the separated or dualist views, is what I call the *duality* view. This combines the one and the many by making a basic distinction within the whole of reality between the divine and the rest, without separating or opposing the two. One dictionary distinction between the two terms is that 'duality' refers to 'having a double nature' (i.e., while preserving an overarching unity), while 'dual' indicates 'separate co-existing elements' (i.e., emphasizes the separation with no suggestion of unity beyond mere co-existence). The difference is subtle but of the greatest importance and will become plainer as we proceed.[6]

Both in history and in logic there seem to be no further basic options. The heart of the cosmologies of all cultures lies within one or other of these three forms, denoted unitive, dualist or duality.

CHAPTER TWO

The Tribal Societies

Our Tribal Ancestors

With these analytic tools in hand let us go back to where our ancestors began, the world of the tribal societies, the world of technologies that were comparatively primitive and of religions that are best called primal. Many tribal peoples had indeed reached notable levels of civilization – in Egypt and Mesopotamia, in India and China, and later in pre-classical Greece and Rome – but their worldviews remained akin to those of their tribal forebears.

True, some tribal technologies were quite complex, and some were remarkable in their ingenuity, in their close observation of nature, and in their clever use of the limited materials of wood and stone, skin and bone, leaf and sap. They started us on the long history of tools and skills, as with the Maori capacity to drill perfect holes in hard greenstone with stone-age drills, or with the Polynesian ability to navigate across the empty spaces of the South Pacific Ocean.

These technologies began the human race on its discovery of its own potential and its capacity to develop the amazing potential of the natural environment. But while they could explore the medicinal value of plants, and build the pyramids in Egypt or the other 'seven wonders of the world', they could not understand the basic physical structure or the chemical interactions of the materials they used. The Australian Aborigine tracker could follow a trail across an apparently featureless desert. He could make and use the boomerang, and I doubt if anyone in the Boeing Corporation could do that, although they can apply scientific knowledge of aerodynamics to produce a jumbo jet airliner. Tribal technologies were still pragmatic, without the theoretical grasp of scientific understanding.

Likewise their religions still belonged to the great family of primal religions. These possessed a plenitude of gods and spirits and were limited to particular peoples and places. But none of these religions could escape their particularities of place and tribe – they could not become missionary and offer universal faiths to all humankind.

This then sketches the starting point for our journey towards the scientific age of sub-atomic particles, DNA molecules and the composition and history of what lies in outer space, and the journey from the primal religions of the tribal family to the world's major faiths. We shall be focusing on the interactions between these two paths, the scientific and the religious, and in particular the Judaeo-Christian religious path.

Encapsulated Cosmology: The Tribals

We now set forth in more detail the characteristic cosmology of these tribal cultures and religions, their view of the whole universe. This embraces the divine, the human and the natural in one interlocked, working system, usually with a hierarchical arrangement. I shall now work through some of the features of an encapsulated cosmology, and I hope you will be able to sense that it is the tribal worlds being described in this generalized way.

1. *There is a single, closed, inclusive system,* embracing the whole of reality, including the gods as part of the cosmos, which they have shaped or produced from within its given materials.

2. *There are fixed, necessary, inherent relations within an organic, symbiotic system.* Each part needs the due operation of the others, with one set of principles or patterns throughout. Hence the earth is a microcosm of the heavens, the macrocosm or normative pattern, as we shall illustrate in a moment. This is how divination can operate by reading off the whole, or the will of the gods, from the part that reflects it, whether this be the patterns on the liver of an animal or in the flight of birds, or in the fall of the bones or whatever when cast by the diviner.

3. *The whole cosmos is intrinsically spiritual or sacred,* either with the status of, or pervaded by the spiritual or divine powers. Plants have emotions and animals can talk; the sun, the moon, trees, earth, and rivers have souls; hoes can work alone; rice and maize are capable of punitive action; the stump of a felled fruit tree is covered lest it be shamed before its fellows; humans, animals and plants can change their natures with the phases of the moon; people can change into animals; the soul can leave the body for long periods while the person still lives; prayer might be directed to any part, and nature worship is not an incorrect term. We call this animism, pantheism, pan-psychism, panentheism or biocosmism – there is *anima* (Latin, 'spirit') potentially everywhere. The world is full of gods and spirits, even if for the moment it may appear to be neutral or some ordinary activities are usually (as we moderns say) secular.[1] Tribal cultures speak of altars and shrines and priests and diviners and sacrifices and prayers; but they have no special word for 'religion' because it is not distinguished from the rest of life.

4. *The inter-relations, status and distinctions between various elements, are uncertain and variable.* A plant or animal may become a totem guardian spirit; a human may be promoted to divinity, or a divinity demoted. The ambivalent divine powers may be favourable today and hostile tomorrow. And there is the constant threat of evil forces to disrupt the system.

5. *The meaning of the cosmos is found within the system;* there is no other source, since it is the sum total of all reality, and includes the gods and spirits.

6. *Society is closed, unitary, sacralized.* This is a localized, highly integrated tribal system, where everyone has a place, limited to biological ancestors, with authority exercised by rulers – chiefs and kings with mystical or divine status – and protected by taboos, as mediators between gods and humans. Sophisticated examples occur in emperor worship (Rome, Japan), and lingered on in the 'divine right of kings' (England, Tsarist Russia).

7. *A nature-orientated, geographical culture of a particular place,* tied to land, the animals, people and spirits living there, and the local language and totems, particular to that people. Places – hills, caves, trees, springs, almost any natural feature – become sacred places, either from their own suggestiveness or from association with some spiritual experience. And each tribal area is seen as 'the centre of the world', superior to all other places.

8. *An a-historical, repetitive, cyclical, mythical view of time.* Hence it is backward-looking, to the ancestors and culture heroes, essentially traditional and

Tribal Encapsulated Cosmology

The Range of Spiritual Powers

SUPREME BEING

High, Sky, or Remote God with/without a Consort or Shrine
Creator, ruler, judge, punisher, etc.

MAJOR DIVINITIES

Departmental: earth, fertility, war, hunting, etc.
With cults and shrines. [Hence 'POLYTHEISM']

LESSER DIVINITIES

Minor departments or functions: iron, smallpox, clan, etc.
With cults and shrines. May be promoted humans.

SPIRITS [Hence 'ANIMISM']

ANGELS: guardian, fallen, or malevolent
SPIRITS: Local/nature spirits in places, objects, animals, etc.
DAEMONS (not devils): local/invasive, wandering, nameless,etc.
FOLKLORE: Fairies, goblins, djinns, harpies, vampires, werewolves.

TOTEMIC SPIRITS

GUARDIANS OF TRIBE/CLAN: Animals, plants, or objects:
Bear, lion, potato, grasshopper, a stone, etc.

ANCESTRAL SPIRITS [Hence 'ANCESTOR WORSHIP']

(a) CULTURE HEROES: legendary/mythical humans with supra-human powers,
or agents of the gods in primeval times.
(b) 'LIVING DEAD' – ANCESTORS, as remembered. Nearer the Spirit powers,
but still human; honoured in cults rather than worshipped;
both loved and feared.

LIVING HUMANS

And THE UNBORN; possibly with Reincarnation.

THE UNDERWORLD

The 'Dead dead', in a vague half-life,
Sheol/Hades, but not 'hell'.

ANIMALS, PLANTS, OBJECTS

in various relations to above,
e.g., Totemism.

conservative. Security lies in the future being 'more of the same', to preserve the system – by its myth stories and renewal rituals (e.g., New Year festivals, new fire festivals.)

9. *Rituals are necessary, vital, manipulative, repetitive.* Done properly, with the right words and sacrifices, they secure harvests, success, etc. This is close to magic; in being efficacious, they work. A traditional sacral leader in Nigeria, the Oni of the city of Ife, in the 20th century asserted that interference with his sacrifices would put the universal course of nature in danger.

10. *Religious knowledge is mystical and unmediated*, communicated directly to the specialists, to whom it is confined as secret and powerful.

11. *Evil is located externally* in angry divinities, evil spirits, demons, or humans (angry ancestors, witches, sorcerers, enemies, black magic).

These are the characteristic features of an encapsulated cosmology. Not all tribal cultures will exhibit all these features but this is the menu, as it were, from which they draw. For the spiritual contents or 'population' of the cosmos another menu is provided in the accompanying chart of the encapsulated cosmos, with its hierarchy from supreme beings through the human to the physical world.

Microcosm of the Macrocosm

There is one aspect of this cosmology that I shall expand because it gives us the feel of this worldview. This is the way in which the lower levels of the system are patterned on the higher. In this way they show how there is a common pattern or set of principles and powers that unite the whole cosmos, across the various divisions or hierarchical levels. It is summed up in terms of nature and humans forming a microcosm which reflects the nature of the highest or divine levels, the macrocosm.

One common dimension of this correspondence view is the belief that the circle is the perfect symbol of the divine. It has neither beginning nor end, and thus represents the eternal. Its constituent parts are entirely uniform in their curvature, there is no irregularity, so it represents unchanging perfection. The sun and the moon, conceived as animated divine beings, are inevitably circular. This principle is exhibited less perfectly but still pervasively in nature. Here almost everything is rounded or at least curved. There are almost no squares and triangles among the rounded pebbles on the seashore, or in the trunks, branches and leaves on the trees and plants.

Animal and human bodies likewise are not made up like a Lego model but are curved and rounded in limb and trunk and head and eye and nostril.

There are famous mediaeval drawings of the human figure itself when stretched out fitting neatly into the cosmic circle. These derived from the great Roman architect, Vitruvius Pollio (first century BCE), who saw the structures of the cosmos repeated not only in the shapes of his temple designs but in the human body.

> ...in the members of the temple there ought to be the greatest harmony in the symmetrical relations of the different parts to...the whole. Then again, in the human body the central point is naturally the navel. For if a man be placed on the flat of his back, with his hands and feet extended, and a pair of compasses centred at his navel, the fingers and toes of his two hands and feet will touch the circumference of a circle described therefrom. And just as the human body yields a circular outline, so too a square figure may be found from it. For if we measure the distance from the soles of the feet to the top of the head, and then apply that measure to the outstretched arms, the breadth will be found to be the same as the height, as in the case of plane surfaces which are perfectly square.[2]

No wonder then that the oldest known sacred buildings in the world, seven millennia old in Assyria, seem to have been circular shrines with domed roofs. If the temple is the dwelling place of the gods on earth then of necessity it must be circular to be appropriate. Likewise not only ancient temples but many Christian church buildings have been circular, an earthly microcosm of the heavenly temple, the macrocosm. The early Jesuit churches in the 16th century were circular, just like the modern Catholic cathedral in Liverpool.

But this microcosmic patterning appears in hosts of other ways in ancient temples. The building itself is orientated towards the east, to the rising of the lord of the heavens, the sun, as later in Christian churches. The proportions and parts of the building may also be governed by macrocosmic consider-ations. Thus the dome or roof is the heavens, the floor is the earth, and the space between is the square human world. Or there are the churches built according to simple mathematical proportions, when the cosmos is regarded

Microcosms of the Macrocosm

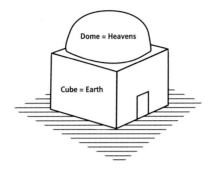

In early Temple structures
(as still in Eastern Orthodox Churches).

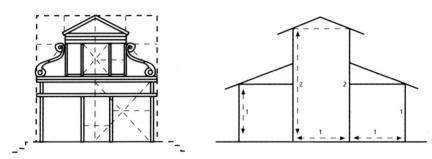

Renaissance Churches

Facade of S. Maria Novella, Florence,
1456, built up of duplication or
division of the basic square unit.

Cross-section of Santo Spirito, Florence,
1436. Simple mathematical ratio of 1:2
governing cross-section of church.

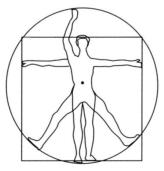

Human
Bodily 'Harmony' with the basic
'Perfect' geometric figures of square
and circle – we fit both.

as itself structured in this way. Renaissance church facades might be built up by duplication or divisions of the basic geometrical square, as in the church in Florence in 1456. Or another church in Florence, in 1436, exhibits a cross-section governed by the simple mathematical ratio of 1:2.

The microcosmic theme is fascinating in its ramifications, but I must restrain my fascination and merely suggest that there is endless evidence of the encapsulated cosmology at work in tribal cultures and surviving on into the highly civilized contexts whence we draw our illustrations. All this spells out the extent to which the tribal cosmology is penetrated and governed by the sacred. It is indeed a sacralized universe, and we must first appreciate this before we can turn to our later and crucial theme, of a de-sacralized universe.

Spirituality of the Primals

But before we start to critique this worldview, I would like to look a little further at some examples of its spirituality, to appreciate its insights and strengths and remove any suggestion of discarding it as merely primitive. An excellent example comes from the Australian Aborigines, whose social structure and technology (despite the boomerang!) may properly be described as primitive or elementary. There is nothing primitive about the following account of worship, using a pearl shell which symbolizes the water from which it comes, and hence water as the mysterious source of life:

> ...each member of the congregation...reverently produced a piece of pearl shell of great beauty, laid it on a cloth which had been spread out, and then gazed at it, chanting quietly and ending with a soft long-drawn-out Ah! – followed by silence...the rapturous hush and intense devotion ...at the Exposition of the pearl shell could only be compared with that at the Catholic service of Benediction when the monstrance is elevated.[3]

To turn to that most forbidding region, Tierra del Fuego, at the bottom of South America: between 1832 and 1834 Charles Darwin made two visits to the Yamana people there, and reported that there were no religious ideas among such miserable and primitive human beings. Anglican missionaries who arrived in 1856 achieved some small results, but concurred with Darwin's attitude. It was not till 1922 that Austrian anthropologists studied the Yamana. They totally surprised a son of one of the founding missionaries, himself married to a Yamana and then nearly 80. They told him about the Yamana belief in a Supreme Being, that they had discovered. He was Lord of Creation and was addressed in prayers as 'my Father', and he needed no sacrifices; but he scarcely appeared in their abundant myths. A profound spirituality had remained undetected for nearly a century.[4]

Similar examples of high spirituality in primitive societies may readily be multiplied, and not least among those Native North American peoples who also remained hunters and gatherers. There is the example of the young man's vigil or 'vision quest', in which he remains in a lonely place with physical and mental disciplines until some transcendent spirit being is revealed as his personal mentor for life. It is not so surprising therefore when a sophisticated, unbelieving anthropologist like the American R.H. Lowie confessed to losing his scepticism about religion after many years of study of the spirituality of such people.[5]

Often quoted is the understanding of God found among another socially and technically primitive people, the hunting and gathering Mbuti or Pygmies of Central Africa..."In the beginning was God, today is God, tomorrow will be God. Who can make an image of God? He has no body. He is as a word that comes out of your mouth. That word, it is no more, it is past, and still it lives! So is God." It is almost superfluous to refer to the 'spiritual' Gospel of St John: "In the beginning was the word, and the word was with God..."

We cannot deny therefore, that the primal religions often exhibited a profound and realistic insight into the fallibilities of the human condition and a recognition of the transcendent spirit realm within the cosmos. In both respects they may be much closer to the truth than the superficial sophisticates of current Western culture.

A brief survey of characteristic Western attitudes to tribal religions over the past three centuries will stand in contrast to the attitude we have adopted here.

- *Primal religions are not really religions at all.* They are just 'mumbo-jumbo' or superstition or 'juju'; this attitude can be documented among Hindus in relation to the tribal peoples of north-west India, among Muslims towards the 'bush illiterates' of Africa, and among Westerners including even Charles Darwin, who antedated the missionaries in thinking the Yamana mentioned above had no religious ideas at all.

- *Primal religions are the work of the devil.* In this view tribal peoples were given the credit of having a religion, but it was radically distorted and corrupted by the wiles of the devil.

- *Primal religions romanticized and idealized.* This unrealistic view stands at the opposite extreme to those above and is the common attitude in much bi/multicultural discussion seeking to rehabilitate the tribal cultures. It is not based on detailed study but on politically-driven ideologies seeking power for minorities.

- *Primal religions as socio-cultural functions.* This attitude has been common in the social sciences, especially anthropology, and reduces religion from something distinctive in its own right, and relating to the transcendent, to a socially-invented tool serving the mundane needs of various societies, such as providing 'an all-purpose social glue' to secure social cohesion.

- *Primal religions are authentic religions* which serve the above social purposes by the very fact that they draw on transcendent resources beyond the social or the merely human, and provide a comprehensive worldview that includes a cosmology. The degrees of truth or falsity in this cosmology will engage us as we proceed, but we start by rejecting all reductionist views – turning religion into something else – and by recognizing its authenticity as genuinely religious.

Reaching Out Beyond the Primals

One could continue with examples of authentically and deeply religious attitudes from tribal cultures with their encapsulated cosmologies, where the spirit world is never far away. Equally significant for what lies ahead in our historical journey, there are signs of dissatisfaction with this too cosy presence of the divine. These appear in the many versions of a reaching out beyond the known universe to some truly transcendent Being, some high god who seems inactive and remote from human affairs, with neither cult, shrine nor image.

Examples occur in most continents: Olodumare among the Yoruba in Nigeria; Wakan Tanka, the Great Spirit, among Native American peoples, and Io among the Maori, assuming that this was a pre-contact belief – an issue that remains controversial.

St Paul visiting Athens noted the same thing – the "altar to the unknown god". And the most moving example I know comes from the Incas, a high civilization in the 16th century in Peru, but still with an encapsulated cosmology like any tribal people. Here is their prayer to the unknown high god:

> O Viracocha, Lord of the Universe:..Can divination be employed to learn
> where thou art? If away, where art thou? Whether thou art above, whether
> thou art below, whether thou art around...O hear me! From the heaven
> above, from the sea below, where'er thou art, O Creator of the world, O
> Maker of man, Lord of all lords, to thee alone, with eyes that fail, with
> longing to know thee, I come to thee...to know thee, to understand
> thee...Thou seest me, thou knowest me; the Sun, the Moon, the day, the
> night, Spring and winter, they all travel...from appointed places to their
> destinations;...Thou holdest them under them under thy sceptre...O
> hear me! Let me be thy chosen; do not suffer that I should tire, that I
> should die.[6]

From three different cultures we can find another image of spiritual longing – that of thirsting-for-water. From the Incas themselves, in one of their hymns of longing, there is this plaint: "To look on thee, like as on a river, like as on the springs, gasping with thirst."[7] And from the Native American Arapaho people, this simple prayer: "Father, have pity on me; I am crying for thirst, there is nothing here to satisfy me." From the Hebrew psalmist in the classic Authorised Version of Psalm 42: "As the hart panteth after the waterbrooks, so panteth my soul after thee, O God."

These internal critiques of a closed cosmos were ineffective. There was no clear revelation or response from such remote, high gods. At best certain elites might claim knowledge of them, as seemingly with the Maori *whare wananga*. But they didn't function in the public cult, with shrines, images, prayers and sacrifices; these things were left to the lesser divinities and other spirits.

Criticism of the Encapsulated Cosmologies

Other critiques arose from the ways in which the known gods created the rest of the universe. This was often from pre-existing raw material – sometimes even from the carcases of other gods whom they had slain! This makes them mere artificers, workmen. Or again creation was from something within themselves, from their own energy or powers or qualities, emanating or oozing out to make a world. Or again, and from themselves, creation occurred by some sexual process, with a consort, or even by masturbation as in some myths. In short, in their creative activities the gods were only too like human beings – mere workmen, with some pretty crude methods, or, as we say, they were too anthropomorphic.

And in their moral lives they were no model for humans. On the issue of sexual activity alone their record would offend sensitive tribal peoples:

> ...the Babylonian god Ishtar seduced a man, Gilgamesh, the Babylonian hero. In Egyptian religion the god Osiris had sexual relations with his sister, the goddess Isis...In Canaan, El, the chief god, had sex with Asherah...In Greek beliefs, Zeus married Hera, chased women, abducted the beautiful young male, Ganymede, and masturbated at other times; Poseidon married Amphitrite, pursued Demeter, and raped Tantalus. In Rome the gods sexually pursued both men and women.[8]

And these were the gods of some of the great early civilizations, albeit still with primal religions. Apart from sexuality, the gods of the tribal peoples were immoral and unreliable in their dealings with humans – they could lie and deceive and make greedy demands for gifts and sacrifices, or prove arbitrary in their favours. At best they remained ambivalent in their relations with the world. Again, they were only too anthropomorphic. With such gods one can start to bargain or even threaten them – as in a Zulu prayer to the effect that if they don't do better by their worshippers, then the sacrifices will be withheld and they can go off and eat grasshoppers!

These moral limitations of tribal religions are illustrated from the very same Inca in Peru whose moving prayer we have listened to. Here is another of their prayers: "O Sun! Grant that these thy children may conquer other people [and]...be conquerors always; for this thou hast created them." And when these imperialists found their prayer answered they sent some of the handsomest captives to their capital for sacrifice to the Sun who had given them the victory.

And of course the very multiplicity of gods and spirits sets the scene for inconsistencies and confusions among human beings, and initiates the search for unitive, monotheistic faiths that we shall be looking at. The encapsulated cosmos, then, was not a comfortable one – what with the many kinds of uncertainty about the divine realm and about its pervasive presence in the world around us. There is an element of insecurity and fear inbuilt into this cosmos, and as we shall see in more specific terms there is no room for science.

Despite these serious defects, however, we have been looking at humanity's common and authentically religious heritage. The whole encapsulated cosmology itself represents a great human achievement – the ability to transcend the animal level and the consciousness of the present moment. The universe is not a chaotic jumble of disconnected and completely random events. In these varied forms of transcendence human beings have managed to combine an immense range of phenomena from daily experience and from the past, the present and the future, the 'one and the many'. They have reached the concept of a 'uni-verse' that hangs together and reveals patterns of behaviour that seem to be reliable. Primal religions in their cultures have enabled the human race to cope somehow with the problems of life and death, and this is not to be despised.

Primal Religions Incompatible with Science

But the encapsulated world could not go beyond pragmatic technologies and initial and abortive scientific forays. It could not develop what we properly call science. There was no room for the rationality, regularity, consistency and coherence in the natural world that we express in the term 'laws of nature' – there was no room for this understanding when the world was permeated by a host of uncoordinated gods and spirits, of ambivalent nature and uncertain temper. One cannot imagine climatology and the scientific study of the weather developing far if the scientist was also bugged by the question: "Will the monsoon make God wet?" – to use the revealing phrase of Kosuke Koyama, the Japanese scholar.

There was no room for the scientific understanding when both the gods and human beings stood in such uncertain relation to the surrounding world of nature, which might serve them well today and threaten to annihilate them tomorrow. By and large there was too much religion in the encapsulated cultures, for there to be room or any basis for science.

This verdict remains true of all religions in this great family of faiths, including the traditional religion of the Maori as a tribal people. To speak of 'Maori Science' as the National Science Curriculum of the New Zealand Ministry of Education tries to do, combines an abuse of terms, and a confusion of technology with science, along with ignorance of the cosmology we have called encapsulated. The sponsoring of such false, ideologically-driven views by a Western government, and the funding of them by the taxpayer, should be publicly exposed; and scholars who know they are false are irresponsible citizens if they don't do so.

CHAPTER THREE

The Axial Religions

Dualist Cosmologies of the Civilizations

Now we are going to turn to the other cosmologies that appeared in critique of this encapsulated worldview. These share several striking features: they all emerge as part of a new religious faith seeking to deal with the felt inadequacies of primal religions; they take shape within a major civilization; these civilizations are separate from one another, and diffusion from one to the other is no explanation; they all arise from known individuals such as founders, prophets, thinkers, and teachers; and they cluster within a particular period of history.

I refer first to the forerunner, the new monotheistic faith introduced into Egypt in the 14th century BCE by the Pharoah, Amenhotep IV, or Akhenaten, or Ikhnaton. He suppressed the state cult of Amon-Re and its many gods, and deleted 'Amon' and the word 'gods' from inscriptions; he built a new capital as centre for the new faith (the modern archaeological site, Tell el Amarna); he designed temples with no microcosmic governing principles, no numinous mystique, but with roofless sanctuaries open to the full light of the Sun as symbol of the one supreme god of all the universe, Aton, who was therefore free of all anthropomorphic representation, yet stood in personal relation to the king.

This religious revolution was accompanied by a revolution in aesthetics wherein a greater realism and simplicity replaced the older conventions, as may be seen in the exquisite head of Nefertiti, his queen. He himself may have been author of a beautiful hymn inscribed on a tomb:

How manifold it is, what thou hast made!...
O sole god, like whom there is no other!
Thou didst create the world according to thy desire,
While thou wert alone...
Whatever is on earth, going upon its feet,
And whatever is on high, flying with its wings.

The countries of Syria and Nubia, the land of Egypt,
Thou settest every man in his place.
Thou suppliest their necessities;
Everyone has his food, and his time of life is reckoned.
Their tongues are separate in speech,
And their natures as well...[1]

The later Inca out-reaching prayer we quoted was in fact both anticipated here and answered in an imperial, public, working religion, that dealt with many of the dissatisfactions of the tribal faiths. But it seems to have come too early and to have been imposed too suddenly and forcefully by royal decree. His successor was the short-lived boy-Pharoah, Tutankhamen, whose magnificent tomb seems to have been the only one to escape the tomb-robbers and caused a sensation when uncovered in 1922. The priests of the displaced faith and the populace soon reverted completely to the old ways. But just think of what Amenhotep's success might have done to the later history of Egypt, and even possibly for science!

The next new faith, Zoroastrianism, appeared among the tribes of what is now the north-east area of Iran and arose from the teachings of the prophet Zoroaster, or Zarathushtra, and from no known external influences. He is of uncertain date: possibly around the same time as Akhenaten in Egypt, or else later in the 6th century BCE. Zoroaster believed he had seen god, Ahura Mazda, the creator of all that is good in creation; he alone was to be worshipped in moral purity. Opposed to this god is an evil deity, at war with

Ahura Mazda, whom we must choose to reject and who will finally be overcome. This one-way view of history seems to have allowed for a good deal of Hindu cyclic views of time in the course of reaching this final goal. The tribal gods were repudiated because of their violent and immoral natures, but various features of tribal religions, such as animal sacrifices, persisted in some syncretist forms of Zoroastrianism.

This new faith replaced the Aryan tribes' polytheistic nature-worship, it converted the king, it probably influenced the religion of the Hebrew and other peoples, and for over a thousand years it was the official religion of successive major empires (Persian, Seleucid, Parthian, and Sassanian), until it succumbed to Islam in the seventh century CE. It now survives with over a hundred thousand worshippers in rural Iran, Bombay (known as Parsees), and a few other places.

The Axial Age

In the century or so before and after the sixth century BCE, a variety of independent leaders seem to have instigated similar revolts against the traditional tribal faiths, and especially against their priesthoods and sacrificial rituals. These individuals ranged from Pythagoras, the early religious philosopher in Greece, to Mahavira, the founder of the Jain religion and also to Gautama the Buddha and those who developed the Hindu Upanishad literature in India, and in China to Confucius and Lao-Tse, the founder of Taoism.

It is certainly remarkable that so many of the great religious developments or faiths of the world should have their roots within this one century and take shape soon afterwards – the great Greek religious philosophy from Pythagoras through Socrates, Plato, and Aristotle to the Stoics, the Jain religion still with some three million in India, Buddhism, Hinduism's finest literature, and in China Confucianism and Taoism. To these, some would add Judaism, with many of its great prophets around this time; and hence in a derivative way Christianity and Islam are said to have their roots in this remarkable tidal wave of religious innovation and reform.

These great faiths are often referred to as the 'world religions' – a misleading term against which I steadily campaign. Since there is no one world religion in the singular, there cannot be a plurality; and the tribal religions, which can be regarded as a world-spanning family or type, are excluded from the term. The simple alteration, to the phrase 'world's religions' solves the problem.[2]

Better to speak of the 'universal religions', in distinction from the essentially local and particular faiths of the tribal cultures. They all move towards a moral and universal, unitive or monotheistic conception of divinity. While most of them have in practice remained either ethnic or regional, it is not total nonsense to conceive of their becoming the religion of all peoples – they are conceivably, potentially and nowadays often intentionally universal – some have been or are now again becoming very missionary. On the other hand, it is nonsense to conceive of Maori or Zulu or a Native American religion becoming universal, and these indigenous peoples do not think like this.

The term 'Axial Age' for these sixth century developments was popularized by the Swiss philosopher Karl Jaspers in 1949 (English translation 1953), and has been used in other schema for the history of religions. It certainly offers a vivid statement of how so many major religious revolutions are focused on this period. It might even be claimed that seven of the new universal or major religions arose in different parts of the world within 50 years of one another. The axial concept and its application to all or only to some of the universal religions, is the issue towards which we are steadily working, and later we shall critique the concept itself. At the same time we may note that there is no corresponding axial concept in the history of science; the reason for this will appear as we proceed.

Features of Axial Age Faiths

But let us first examine in a summary and necessarily over-simplified way some of the main characteristics of this widespread revolution:

1. It is marked by the *outstanding individuals* I have named, and through them it presents a sustained and penetrating critique of the tribal faiths they rejected or reformed. Thinkers, philosophers, teachers, they provide the first great critique of religions in the name of better, deeper, truer religion. They expressed their critiques and their new teachings in literatures that still provide the scriptures of the new faiths. They were not atheists, secularists, or anti-religious. True, atheists and secularists can be found as minorities in these ancient as in modern times, but they did not leave their mark on the world in new cultures as did these religions.

Historical Chart of the Religions

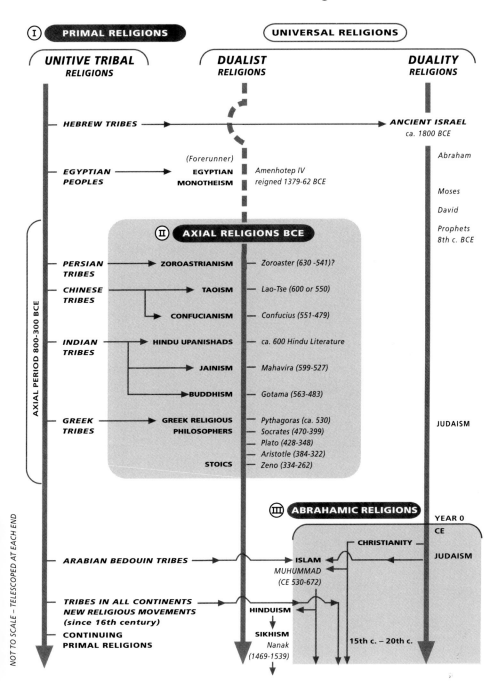

2. This sustained reflection and self-critique amounted to a great *spiritualization of religion*. The vast outward ritual systems, with elaborate animal and other crude forms of sacrifice, controlled by powerful and often corrupt priesthoods exploiting the worshippers, these were rejected for personal prayer and meditation, and more ascetic individual disciplines and lifestyles. The Upanishads in Hinduism bypassed the need for public ritual and introduced the disciplines of yoga to relate to divinity. The Hebrew prophets attacked the public temple cultus as no alternative to social justice, and the Psalmist speaks of God valuing a clean heart rather than animal sacrifice.[3]

3. Correlative with this is the *moralization of religion* that dealt with some of the crudities we have already noted in primal religions. Zoroaster with his moral purity, Mahavira among the Jains with a moral order that demanded respect for all animal, even insect, life, Confucius with his moral demands on politicians and in everyday life, the Hebrew prophets and the Greek philosophers – all these were conspicuously preachers of ethics. I once taught a course on Aristotle's *Ethics*, for it is still often a set book in moral philosophy – or I hope it is, for his ethics of virtue is having somewhat of a revival.

4. Also congruent with these developments is the widespread *unitive and monotheistic tendency* that makes these faiths at least potentially universal. In place of the confusing and uncertain polytheistic world of gods many and spirits innumerable, these faiths presented some kind of single, supreme, ultimate being or power that operated in a more regular way and applied to all nations. Although most of these new faiths in practice remained within their original ethnic boundaries, or expanded into neighbouring peoples and then stopped, they were and remain trans-ethnic in principle. In the 20th century some revealed their trans-ethnic capacity in practice, as with Asian faiths making small inroads into Western or European peoples. Their more unitive view of divinity and of humanity is allied with an understanding that there is a 'uni-verse', a single cosmic system. Something like this seems to be essential for the development of science, and we shall be examining whether this was followed up.

5. All these faiths (again, possibly excepting Judaism) *developed within the existing great civilizations*. It was probably the new problems that emerge in large urban areas, with complex political, economic and technological systems, that prompted much of the critique of the old and now inadequate tribal religions. The new faiths provided the dynamics for social change, and

cultural development. As the sociologist of religion Max Weber has spelled out – they were no mere reinforcements or sanctioners of existing societies, in the manner of Durkheim and Malinowski, or as might be said, of primal cultures.

It is therefore all the more remarkable that the revolutions and advances of the Axial Age did not lead to the development of science. The wealth, the economic needs, the highly organized cities, individuals with leisure, sophisticated thinking that could critique the tribal worldviews, great achievements in poetry, drama and art, even initial contributions to the later development of science; they were all there. There was sufficient technology to make the apparatus for experiments, sufficient mathematics for measurement and calculation – these were all present. But science in the proper sense of the term had to wait two more millennia. The answer to this problem will tell us a great deal; so we must first see if it was really like this, and if so, then why?

Science and Technology

To do this requires a clarification of terms, and especially the fundamental distinction between science and technology. This distinction was first denied on a massive scale in modern times when the Marxist state took over the central and political control of science and dictated the desired practical or technological results, to which even scientific theory had to adjust. Views similar in principle have spread in our Western societies to attack the distinction between polytechnics and universities.

This approach dominates our politicians, and the funds dispensed annually by state foundations for research, science and technology in many Western countries. For example, and as might be expected in New Zealand's pragmatic culture, the primary emphasis is on research that will increase export earnings and job opportunities. New Zealand didn't produce its Lord Ernest Rutherford on that philosophy.

The same attitude emerges in those scientists who define their work in terms of social need and practical value. The then Minister of Education in New Zealand gave notorious expression to this view of science when he declared in 1993 that in no sense was his own doctoral research in animal husbandry, or that of his colleagues, concerned with finding out the truth about reality!

It was this confusion between science and technology, especially in the Soviet Union, that first drove the distinguished physical chemist, Michael Polanyi, into the defence of scientific and academic freedom in the 1930s, and then into his major study of the philosophy of science. He has often written on the difference between science and technology. So I shall simply summarize in some of his terms: "Technology is knowledge of the way to produce practical advantages by the use of material resources."

The Maori stone-age craftsman impresses by his ability over several months to drill a hole in greenstone, whether for use as an axe or an ornament; but this is superseded when the different possibilities of steel material and the electric drill arrive. "Science, on the other hand, cannot be affected in its validity by variations" in our needs or our materials. "Nothing will become untrue that was true before – nor the reverse" – for these reasons.[4] Science is concerned with knowledge for its own sake, with truth as such, whether or not it has any practical application. Technology is utilitarian, and may even proceed successfully, as it often has done, on the basis of false scientific beliefs.

A simple illustration: there have been amazing improvements in our means of illumination since the 18th century. From the candle and the oil lamp, the technology of lighting has advanced through coal gas flares, incandescent gas mantles, electric arcs, the filament lamp, to fluorescent tubes – and whatever is next in the research or development pipeline. Most of this advance has occurred through trial and error, as with Edison, although sometimes scientific knowledge of the physics of materials has helped. But I understand that all this has contributed nothing to the scientific, theoretical understanding of that most fundamental and mysterious of physical phenomena – light itself.

Despite the contributions of Paul Dirac and quantum theory, scientists still wrestle, I believe, with the full reconciliation of the alternative wave and particle views of the behaviour and structure of light, and wonder what it might mean to speak of 'wavicles'. And if and when this is resolved it will probably have no immediate application to the technology of illumination. But it will be an immense illumination to our understanding of the universe and to the wonders of sheer knowledge itself.

Likewise, in the theory of numbers there is a theorem by the most distinguished mathematician of the 17th century, the Frenchman, Pierre de

Fermat; it is called Fermat's Last Theorem, and its full proof has been sought in vain ever since. This proof was finally reached in the early 1990s by Professor Andrew Wiles and, as he said, it is of no practical value whatsoever. But it will be a sad day when no one thrills to this great intellectual achievement in its own right.[5]

It is true, of course, that advancing technology can assist, and may even be essential in the confirmation of, the work of theoretical science, and that advances in the latter may suggest advances in technology that the technician would never dream of. All this can occur in an ad hoc manner but for the present it seems that the theoretical relation between the two remains as contingent as I have sketched it.

Egyptian Achievements

Armed with this distinction, we can now examine the great civilizations associated with the Axial Age in terms of technology and science. A brief look first at the civilization of Egypt within which the remarkable monotheism of Akhenaton appeared. Other remarkable achievements included the invention of hieroglyphics, a "highly developed form of phonetic writing...possibly the greatest intellectual feat of all recorded history", representing "the reflective symbol-making powers of the mind."[6]

Similar imaginative achievements did not occur in the practical realms of mathematics, of arithmetic for trade and geometry for such gigantic projects as the pyramids. It took 27 hieroglyphic signs to write 999, even more complicated than Roman numerals. Practical ways of working out mathematical problems predominated, and might be remarkably accurate. Thus:

> The Egyptian way of calculating the area of a circle by squaring eight-ninths of the diameter is worthy of admiration as it implies a value of 3.1605 for π, a rather good approximation. Yet, the accomplishment cannot be considered science, but only a piece of protoscience in which statements and procedures are not generalized and supported by proofs.[7]

As for the pyramids, they exhibit both technical ingenuity and backwardness. Without knowledge of pulleys, or wheeled carts adequate for such huge blocks, these engineers managed not only to shape the blocks without hard metal tools to accuracies of one fiftieth of an inch, but to lift them in their thousands by wooden sleds and ramps to great heights. Jaki points out similar contrasts in the medical arts, which show:

> ...the first rudiments of medical terminology, the first use of bandages, the pioneering of anatomical investigations, and the first listing of some truly useful, naturally available drugs...But...medical practice remained ...intermingled with an enormous mass of senseless, magical and animistic notions. The marvellous recognition of the parallelism between the various lesions of the brain and the functional losses in different parts of the body did not give second thoughts to ancient Egyptian physicians. They persisted...with the belief that the cause of sickness was an animistic force or spirit...[8]

Many other contrasts can be identified, such as the obsession with animals in their art and their religion, combined with no attempt at any systematic classification or study that could show the beginnings of biology. Their religious worldview still included the primal, animistic, polytheist religious type retained from the earlier peoples of the Nile valley or imported in the Osiris cult that ensured the fertility of the crops.

Later religion in the dynastic period of the Pharoahs became focused on the Sun god and his child the god-king; this led to "one of the most remarkable spectacles in history to see all the resources of a great culture and a powerful state organized, not for war and conquest, not for the enrichment of a dominant class, but simply to provide the sepulchre...of the dead Kings" in the pyramids.[9] This remarkable concentration on death and the afterlife mitigated against the concern and curiosity about this world that leads to science, and corresponded to the dualism of the Axial faiths. The excursus into strict monotheism of Amenhotep IV might have provided the necessary scientific concept of a single universe and of fresh interest in this world, but it was too short-lived to be developed in a scientific direction.

Greek Achievements
Greece is usually credited with the birth of science. Here I can but skim over the catalogue of amazing achievements, which can be followed up in any encyclopaedia. In mathematics, Hipparchus' development of trigonometry,

and Euclid's geometry that has lasted into our own times, and Archimedes' measurement of the surfaces and volumes of curved figures and much more. Earlier there had been the belief in the mathematical foundations of reality and structure of divinity propounded by Pythagorus (ca. 570-500 BCE) in his religious brotherhoods; some such idea is basic to modern science.[10]

In astronomy, three major discoveries were made in two or three generations, not in the number of facts available but in mental curiosity and theoretical explanations:

1. The sphericity of the earth (Pythagorus), and that by a remarkable advance of thought, it does not rest or float on anything (Anaximander, fl. 6th. c.)

2. Aristarchus of Samos (fl. ca. 270) founding theoretical mechanics and the first to propose a heliocentric view of the earth and the sun, and setting out to measure, and fairly accurately, their distance apart, and their relative sizes. This enables a true explanation of solar and lunar eclipses.

3. Hipparchus' (fl. 146-27) discovery of the "precession of the equinoxes". In accurate noting of the positions of the stars he found substantial discrepancies from those recorded in Alexandria and Babylonia centuries earlier. He gave a value of about 45" for the annual changes, as compared with 50".26 accepted nowadays. His work enabled remarkably close calculations of the length of the year.

Then there was Aristotle, setting out to organize and systematize the whole field of knowledge and making profound contributions in biology, even if he did successfully reassert the geocentric view of the universe. And in anatomy and physiology there was Galen, whose complete physiological scheme lasted until three centuries ago. And in the field of technology there were the achievements of architecture, and even the harnessing of steam power to open temple doors, and of waterwheels with geared transmssions for power. The theory and practice of the five basic machines of mechanics were well understood – the lever, the wedge, the wheel, the pulley and the screw. Archimedes' water screw is still used to raise water in the Middle East.

Why, oh why then, did Greece, which started so much, not lead on into the development of science? We shall answer this later in a comprehensive way that applies to most of the other Axial faiths. But we can stop for two signs of basic defects. Aristotle the scientist and noted biological observer, believed women were inferior to men, less complete or developed, as it were. He argued deductively from this premise that they therefore would have fewer teeth than men! Although he was married twice he never thought to count the teeth of either of his wives! Some Greek observation and measurement of nature had severe limits, especially when controlled by such preconceived theories.

The other more serious illustration lies in the great astronomical system of Ptolemy, supported by massive observations of the heavens by his technology – the ingenious instruments he invented, and by his mathematical skills. And it worked for over 15 centuries, predicted eclipses, and enabled the 15th and 16th century European explorers to circumnavigate the globe.

But its premises were simply wrong. The heavenly bodies were not animate, intelligent, perfect and eternal divine beings, that therefore had to move in a perfect, circular fashion. His basic circle-upon-circle, epicycle-upon-epicycle astronomical plan of the heavens was based on this theological premise, and the observations were all interpreted to fit the theory. There was no way of marrying this to the systems of Copernicus and Kepler. These had to start from quite different premises that we shall be uncovering. Ptolemaic astronomy was not science. It was in a sense applied theology, and wrong theology, and that was where its trouble lay.

Indian Achievements

We can raise the same questions about the great civilization associated with the Axial Age religions in India. Here the story is much less varied than in Greece. Both the mathematical concept of zero and the system of place value for numerals and for decimals, two of the great scientific discoveries, seem to have been known in India; but the concentrations were on astronomy, physiology and psychology. There was much reasoning and observation in astronomy, as in what has been called:

> that little gem of ancient Hindu astronomy, the *Aryabhatiya* of Aryabhata
> ...the earliest known Indian mathematical and astronomical text bearing
> the name of an individual author. A metric composition of some 120
> lines, it was intended to serve as a capsule formula for the principal
> results of astronomical knowledge toward the end of the fifth century
> A.D. ...the work reveals the keen, progressive mind of its author, who
> seems to have recognized the rotation of the earth on its axis... the work

also shows that the cyclic ages and the calculations of their lengths in terms of Brahma's life-span were of fundamental importance even to Aryabhata, the most scientifically inclined figure of early Hindu astronomy...He took pains to fix the date of the Kaliyuga [one of the cyclic Ages, variously estimated at from 1200 to 1200x360 years]...on the great Bharata battle in 3102 B.C. Needless to say, such precision reflects not scientific accuracy but...mythological cosmology...The fact that he made room for such details in an extremely short compendium of astronomy should speak for itself.[11]

In medicine there were various detailed medical treatment systems; but there was no experimentation, except in psychology and associated psychosomatic techniques, as in *yoga*, for the mastery of mind over body. The most striking technological achievements were represented by the pillar of pure iron at Delhi and the still-unexplained rustless iron pillars of the emperor Asoka. Modern science in India has been imported from the West.

Chinese Achievements

China also has its Axial Age religions and a notable history of inventions, and like Greece, of aborted scientific initiatives. All this is set forth in learned detail in the successive volumes since 1954 by Joseph Needham and his collaborators, entitled *Science and Civilization in China*. Even if we concentrate upon the older China that was contemporaneous with the Axial Age there is a notable technological record, especially in engineering – water-power for industry, iron and steel technology, suspension bridges, hydraulic engineering in general, and mechanical clockwork.

Careful observation and recording are essential to science and common in Chinese records. Thus they were early discussing the hexagonal nature of snowflake crystals. Needham indeed asserts that their discovery of zero, of negative numbers and decimal place values was earlier than in India, as were optics, acoustics and magnetism, with knowledge of magnetic compasses.

All this is a mere selection from the vast detail in Needham's volumes. But the verdict is given by Needham himself in another work when he is forced to assert "the undeniable fact that *modern* science was born in Europe and only in Europe."[12] He can use the term 'science' in the title of his Chinese volumes only in some non-modern sense that approximates to technology.

The great civilizations of Egypt, Greece, India and China, therefore, with their associated Axial Age spiritual developments, exhibit clever technologies and contributions preparatory to the development of science, but never proceeded to develop what we mean by this term. To explain this impasse, we shall examine some further characteristics of Axial Age cosmologies.

Axial Critique of the Encapsulated Cosmos

Christopher Dawson, the notable historian of culture in the middle of the 20th century, takes a more critical view and sees the Axial Age much less as a progressive, spiritual breakthrough. For him, it is primarily a disillusioned rejection of the unitive, encapsulated cosmos as a manifestation of the divine powers. This critical attitude was, he claims, manifest in Egyptian literature several centuries before Akhenaten's monotheism, and about the same time in Babylonia. This was well before the so-called Axial Age.

It meant a rejection of the earlier cosy cosmos where everything was accepted as sacred in some sense, with its alleged patterns and powers running through it all, and so uniting the microcosmos with the macrocosmos – this view is a mockery in the light of all the disparities, injustices, suffering and evil in the world. Here was a realistic revolt, with a sense of the dualism between what is all around us and what it ought to be like. Dawson refers to the poem of the Righteous Sufferer, the so-called Babylonian Job, which like its parallel in the Hebrew scriptures, is a defiant challenge to the current worldview.

This critique represents something more than the desire for greater spirituality and moral reform and for the universality of a unitive godhead, the features we have identified in the Axial faiths. It brought about a more radical revolution wherein a new superior world was envisaged – a higher, absolute, unchanging, more spiritual reality. By contrast, the ever-changing, unreliable, dying and passing away daily life around us has little reality and no real worth.

The Dualist Alternative

We can identify the new dualist teaching as ascetic in relation to this world. This was seen first in India, with the Hindu Brahman purging his soul from the world of *maya*, of appearances, by a kind of Socratic discipline; or the holy man who disciplines his mind and body by becoming a hermit, fasting motionless, speechless and with no recognition of others, and abandoning his mind to an ever-deepening dreamlike state. The various forms of yoga in India are lesser forms of the same spiritual discipline.

Dawson regards these as forms of personal salvation, found in Hinduism and Jainism, but supremely in Buddhism. Here:

> ...existence is bound to the wheel of birth and death, of suffering and desire. Not only is this human life an illusion, but the life of the gods is an illusion, too, and behind the whole cosmic process there is no under-lying reality...there is only the torture-wheel of sentient existence and the path of deliverance, the 'via negativa' of the extinction of desire which leads to Nirvana – the Eternal Beatific Silence.[13]

At first sight, all this seems far removed from the Greek attitude to life, and the curiosity about the natural world that led them into the beginnings of science. Even for Aristotle, who contributed so much to the development of the scientific attitude, matter was of secondary status, marked by accidental and capricious features. And for Plato, nature was an unreal shadow of the real. As Dawson puts it:

> It was from the golden mouth of Plato that the vision of the two worlds, the world of appearance and of shadows, and the world of timeless, changeless reality, found classic expression...(and then in Plato's words) "the other world of the eternal forms...not clogged with the pollutions of mortality and all the colours and vanities of human life...not enshrined in that living tomb which we carry about...imprisoned in the body like an oyster in its shell."[14]

This is the dualism between the spiritual and the material worlds that took possession of the great cultures of the Levant and of India. It may be identified in a wide range of polarities that are still with us: the spiritual and the physical; theory and practice; form and content; mind and matter; body and soul; time and eternity; intellect and the senses; the rational and the irrational; reality and appearance; this worldly and other-worldly, and in some uses the sacred and the secular. All these are seen as polar opposites, at the one pole the goodies, at the other pole, the baddies!

Variations in China and Persia

In China the dualism was not 'horizontal' between higher and lower but rather a vertically running dualism of polarity between opposite principles or powers. The supreme polarity was between the Yin and the Yang, which modelled and controlled everything else in opposite pairs. The Yang embraced everything round, dry and weightless, which might be seen as physical qualities for scientific examination. But this vanishes when the Yang correlates them with its other non-physical principles of peace, eating, wealth, cheerfulness, celebrity and profit! Likewise the Yin embraces everything square, wet and heavy – again, physical qualities. But what have these to do with sorrow, drinking, poverty, ignominy and decapitation (sic)?

I don't think the modern feminist movement in China will be enamoured of their identification with the feminine Yin and a portfolio that includes square, heavy, drinking and decapitation! There is no intelligible order or empirical relationships discernible in this arbitrary jumble of concepts. It must have been one of the main barriers to the development of any systematic scientific work, despite the advanced technology and preparations for science that were present in China.

China's dualism reveals that there are various forms of dualism. Some of these occurred in Persia, in Zoroastrianism. There, dualism took forms too complex to expound here. These included something of the Greek higher/lower dichotomy, and added a moral dualism in which we share in the conflict between a good and an evil divinity, who will finally be overcome by the former. There are echoes of Judaeo-Christian views here, and it is possible that Persian beliefs wielded specific influences in the development of biblical cosmology. We need not attend further to this since it was the different, and decidedly more rational, Indo-Greek form that dominated Western culture.

Impersonal Ultimates and Absolutes

Associated with these various dualisms, there is another and equally striking difference from the world of the tribal encapsulated cosmologies. These were permeated by the gods and spirits in only too human or personal forms. But we also noticed the reaching out for more unified and refined concepts of the divine. This was evident in the personal supreme being to whom such eloquent prayers were addressed by diverse tribal peoples. But these aspirations have not been taken as a cue, rounded out and established in the higher, spiritual realms of these dualist systems. Instead, the opposite was effected and the personal was virtually eliminated from ultimate reality.

The early Egyptian monotheism of Akhenaten did seem to have involved a personal relation between the sun-god Aten and the Pharoah, but this faith was aborted. Amid the complexities of Zoroastrianism in Persia there may have been a personal dimension to the Supreme being, but equally it was seen as an original principle of light rather than a warm and loving divinity. There was nothing personal about the dualistic Yin/Yang ultimate structure and power or principle in China; just at best a complementarity of concepts.

Axial Age developments in the religious literature of India remain dominated by the de-personalized model of the holy hermit, the religious specialist, rejecting the social and material worlds and the operations of his own psyche, and focusing instead on the impersonal, eternal, absolute reality of Brahman – a drastic spiritualization of religion by absorption into the Ultimate that represented the cultural ideal.

True, the Upanishad literature of around the sixth century BCE also drastically spiritualized the religion for ordinary folk; it replaced ritual sacrifice conducted by priests for the uninitiated with a higher way of union with the Absolute, using techniques of personal meditation and discipline, such as yoga that gave direct access to the divine, and which any layman can learn. It also recognized 'the bankruptcy of polytheism', and unified the over-populated divine realm into a single Being, Brahman, with which the individual sought identification.

But this supreme Being was beyond change, beyond good and evil, devoid of much that we mean by the personal. In so far as Brahman was conceived as an intelligible being, rejoicing in its blissful self-existence, it was more personal than the ultimate beings of the Greek philosophers. But there was no room for personal relations between god and worshipper, for the soul absorbed into Brahman lost all distinct identity. On the other hand, the really personal relations found between Krishna and Arjuna in the epic story in the Bhagavadgita appear at the end of the Axial Age. This development, like the later Bhakti devotional cults and the much later non-dualist teachings of Ramanuja, stand in counterpoint with the dominant Hindu tradition; it had little direct influence upon the history of the West, and none upon the development of science.

The similar impersonal nature of the new dualist Greek cosmology is best seen in Plato. His working world is as full of gods as for any traditional Greek, from the major gods of Mt Olympus down to local and ancestral divinities. But when it comes to his philosophy and its cosmology his ultimate Idea of the Good is never called a god. Christian thinkers and others have tried to enlist Plato in their service by identifying his Idea of the Good with their God, but an Idea is not a person, not even a soul; at best it is an impersonal, abstract power or principle. Calling it 'The Good' doesn't make it God.

It is no different for Aristotle. In the theory of motion in his physics there had to be a spirit power responsible for each body in motion – no less than 55 such astral divinities accounted for the motions of the heavenly bodies, and above these there was the ultimate Unmoved Prime Mover which they all emulated. But though the Prime Mover was equivalent to ultimate divinity for Aristotle, in no sense was it personal, nor did it serve any religious purpose for a community of worshippers. Such a being is utterly transcendent, could love nothing less than itself, if it could be called love, and is a stranger to the interrelations involved in communion with the likes of us.

Perhaps the nearest the Greek philosophers came to a personal divinity is found in the *Hymn to Zeus* by Cleanthes (331-232), the second leader of the Stoics. God, the *logos*, who abode in the sun, was an intelligent and rational providence vitalizing the universe, and permeating the Stoic himself. The following extracts suggest the emphasis on reason, law and order:

> Most glorious of the immortals, thou of many names, ever all-powerful Zeus, ruler of nature, steering all things with law, hail!...Nor is there any work upon the earth apart from thee...except what evil men do in their own folly...Grant that we may find that judgment, in which thou trusting steerest all things with justice.[15]

Such a refined philosophy never led to worshipping communities, but was more influential in the realms of law and ethics. While it was unitive in the sense of one 'god' and of a single universe it remained within the old unitive, encapsulated cosmology that lies behind belief in divination by the flight of birds and weather portents. This revealed the continuing microcosmic/macrocosmic system of the primal faiths. Science could not be developed within this worldview.

These Axial Age faiths, therefore, and the Greek religious philosophers, reacted in an extreme fashion from the polytheism and crudely anthropomorphic, unreliable divinities and spirits of the tribal cosmologies. From being over-anthropomorphic, only too human, the gods became sub-human in the sense of being impersonal. What was a distinct reform and advance in one dimension was retrograde in another.

And so it is no wonder that new imported mystery cults flourished to fill the gap with their divinities. The ancient cults of the Greek tribes gave way to cults of personal salvation. In Orphism, the soul was progressively enlightened as it freed itself from the defilements of bodily existence. Any encyclopaedia will tell of the Eleusian mysteries, of Mithraism, Isis and Osiris from Egypt, and of the later Gnosticism and the Manichaeans from Persia.

CHAPTER FOUR

The Hebrew Revolution:
De-sacralization

That the Axial de-personalization of the Ultimate Being or Reality had a negative relation to the development of science, can best be shown by turning to the one religion often included in the Axial group, but which we have virtually ignored. This is the religion of the Hebrews, which exhibits four of the characteristics of the Axial reforms:

1. Critical individual thinkers like Job, the Psalmist and others.
2. An emphasis on inward spirituality rather than outward observances of ritual sacrifice and temple cult.
3. The requirement of public and personal morality so prominent in the prophets from the eighth century on.
4. The replacement of polytheism by a monotheistic move towards one supreme and universal ultimate being.

In at least the second, third and fourth features, Hebrew religion could equal if not excel most of the other Axial faiths.

A Personal Supreme Being

In the fourth and last of these, however, the Hebrew faith also stands in clear contrast to the others. Polytheism and the spirits rejected? Yes! One ultimate supreme being for the whole universe? Yes; or if not in their earlier history, then certainly by the mid-millennium. But this one supreme God was intensely personal without being merely anthropomorphic, or only too like mortal, erring humanity. In the Genesis story he walks in the Garden of Eden in the cool of the evening, and talks with the man and the woman, but he never loses his authority, dignity, sovereignty, lordship, wisdom or moral perfection. He is never seen as arbitrary or inconsistent, even if his ways are past finding out and a Job cannot unravel them. While none can see his face and live, he is still a personal god who creates, loves, blesses, judges, saves.

There is an excellent account of the uniqueness of the God of the Hebrews by Lloyd Geering, and I cannot do better than quote:

> ...God, the creator and foundation of all reality, is unlike anything that man had previously worshipped. God is impossible to describe or portray. No man can ever see God...God cannot be manipulated or mastered...The God of Israel could not even be adequately named... when Moses asked for the name...he was told, 'I AM WHO I AM'. In contrast with the indescribable Nirvana [of Buddhist thought], the attributeless Brahman [of Hindu thought], the eternal Tao... [of Chinese thought], the God of Israel could be *heard*.[1]

To this we might add that Israel's God is no Yin-Yang complementary principle (as in Chinese thought), no Idea of the Good or Prime Mover (of Greek thought) – but a coherent, consistent, rational, living Being in personal relation with his creation and his creatures.

A Duality Cosmology, Yet No Science

But why do I stress this difference from the other religions in the context of our enquiry about religion and science? Just this: the Hebrew conviction is that the world around us is made by this kind of good, rational and consistent creator. It therefore reflects its maker and so is itself morally, rationally and consistently ordered. And we ourselves as creatures also reflect our maker with minds that can work rationally and consistently and so be capable of understanding a universe structured in the same way. These related forms of order and coherence are prerequisites for science. And they are lacking from the Axial faiths, with their impersonal ultimate realities, and their dualistic depreciation of this world around us.

The Hebrew cosmology clearly distinguished this temporal world from the eternal world of the Creator, but possessed a positive attitude towards it as both good and orderly. I described this position as a duality in contrast to a dualism, and indicated that the term 'dualism' suggests separation and even opposition between the two spheres; 'duality' rather indicates a distinction without separation or opposition, a distinction within an overarching unity. The difference between these two terms, and the cosmologies they designate, will be the crunch point for our critique. But let us continue to approach it step by step.

Now if the Hebrew people had an alternative to dualism, and so were well equipped with the prerequisites for science, why is it that they show no sign of science, nor do they contribute technical achievements?

Their background is that of pastoral semi-nomads, and when they come to build a temple for their capital they have to import Phoenician architects and artisans from a sophisticated civilization. They remained a pastoral people with minor agriculture, in a poor land with few natural resources and limited economic development, with comparatively few commercial products for a trading exchange that brought stimulating interaction with other societies.

They continued as a semi-tribal, small-scale society without great cities and specialized classes or leisure class, a petty people who spent most of their history at the mercy or under the sovereignty of the great civilizations that rose and fell around them. Their achievements lay more in language and literature, in the legends, stories, poetry, songs and psalms found in smaller tribal societies.

The Hebrews therefore stood in contrast to the Axial faiths of that millennium. They enjoyed borrowed skills from the great civilizations but did not advance beyond elementary technology to science; the Hebrews had the cosmology for science but lacked the more developed technology of the civilizations. They also lacked the sophistication in mathematics that developed in the major civilizations and that is necessary for scientific advance.

Does this mean that all these dimensions are necessary – adequate technology and mathematics, the resources of a powerful civilization, and the right kind of cosmology and religion? So it would seem, and so it would appear to have been when we come to examine the science proper that developed so strikingly from the 16th century in the West. And with the later resources of this advanced civilization, members of the Jewish faith might be said to have come into their own as scientists.

Hebrew Religion not in the Axial Group

However this may be, there is a serious confusion in classifying Hebrew religion, or its successor Judaism and by implication the further Christian and Islamic developments, among the religions of the Axial Age. Despite the features held in common the contrasts are too fundamental, especially the replacement of dualism by duality. Not only are these differences overlooked, but the history of the Hebrew religion is distorted to fit the Axial concept. Essentially this concept asserts that there was a quantum leap in religion about the middle of the first millennium BCE, and that this was associated with a series of remarkable founders or reformers who often gave their name to the faiths that ensued.

Hebrew religion, on the contrary, developed by a long process from the known historical figure of Abraham early in the second millennium BCE, through the towering personality of Moses, the judges and then the kings, especially David, and lastly the prophets and the freedom fighters against successive occupying powers. This is a remarkable story of an obscure people, with remarkable individuals of many kinds through two millennia, yet none of whom founded a new religion.

It is a cooking of the evidence to force this story of a whole people over two millennia into the alien straitjacket of Axial Age theory, and to tele-scope the story into a few centuries in the middle of the second of these millennia, and then to focus it on a few prophets who happen to appeal to modern Western culture, and to miscall this Judaism. Hebrew history has little to do with whatever the Axial Age phenomena may have to tell us. If Hebrew religion was axial in human history, then this was in a different sense and at a different point, that the Axial Age theorists would mostly repudiate.

Duality: A Contingent and De-sacralized World

I have identified three related and unique features of the Hebrew cosmology that serve as prerequisites for science. I have coupled this with a duality that relates this world and the divine realms positively, instead of a dualism that separates and opposes them. The full implications of this duality, in distinction from a dualism, must now be explored. I do so in terms of the two concepts of contingency and of de-sacralization. These complete the prerequisites necessary for science; and they mark out Hebrew religion even more clearly from the Axial group. Let us now explore these basic features in some detail.

In the encapsulated view the worlds of nature, of humanity and of the divine were interwoven and the gods and spirits were all-pervasive and were explanatory of everything that happened. Events in the microcosm, the earthly world, either reflected the spiritual principles of the macrocosm, the heavenly realm, or else they were governed by the whims and fancies of arbitrary or offended spirits. Either way, what happened, and whatever order it displayed, was tied to the sacred powers. There was an inherent or necessary connection. All explanations were ultimately religious.

There was therefore no room for a scientific explanation. There was no realm of nature that operated consistently according to its own forms of order or of law. What served as a stone for practical use in building might become the dwelling place of a spirit power dominating the builder. An ordinary animal to be hunted might be transformed into the totem or guardian spirit of a tribe, with a kind of sacredness. A god might be demoted and a human be promoted. There was no stable, reliable order or security in the form of a hierarchy from things, plants and animals, through humans to the gods and spirits.

In contrast to this, we find the Hebrew understanding of the natural realm as itself created in an orderly, rational fashion that is maintained consistently because its author is both rational and consistent. The creation story in Genesis ch.1 sets out for us this picture of an orderly, hierarchical universe structured from that basic physical reality of light through the material, plant and animal worlds to those of humans and the Creator.

But this is only the first part of the Hebrew relationship between creator and creation. In an ordered and stable world, science would now be possible but it would still be unnecessary. If the order and rationality of nature simply derived from and matched the order and rationality of the divine creator then there would be a direct, inherent, and necessary relationship between them.

The nature of things and how they work in the world could be deduced from the nature and workings of God. And then we would be back to where we were in the encapsulated cosmology. Nature would be a very specific earthly microcosm or copy of the divine macrocosm. All explanations would be theological, and so science would be unnecessary.

The Creator's Freedom in an Open, Contingent Universe

The exit from such an impasse lies in one of the basic characteristics of a rational, personal divinity that I have not named so far. A personal Being is distinct from a divine automaton or robot, or an impersonal abstract principle or impersonal power grinding away in its fixed mode, as in some of the Axial systems. A personal god has freedom and responsibility.

This personal Creator is sovereign over all the potentialities for a creation and freely chooses one form of rationality and order rather than another. The particular rational order that has been chosen and embodied in this created world can be discovered only by going out and studying the world. We can't study the divinity, master how it works, the one way it has to work (as it were), and then deduce how the created realm likewise just has to be shaped and has to work. We cannot discover the speed of light, or whether water expands or contracts when it freezes, or any of the multitudinous specific facts of nature, by any amount of theological study of God. That is why we need science. Aristotle should have counted the teeth of his wives instead of deducing from his theology how the Prime Mover must have made them.

This freedom in creation was expressed when the orderly forms of our world were originally chosen. And further: these orderly forms are not themselves a closed system; besides reflecting the rationality and consistency of their creator, they also reflect the creator's freedom. Within the structures of the natural order, there are potentialities for change and for new forms to appear. Freedom and openness therefore appear in the ongoing operation of the world. Closed, inherently necessary relations between Creator and creation would be very different from open, free relations; would in fact be quite oppressive.

Diogenes Allen has likened the creation to the work of a novelist:

We cannot predict what a character in a novel will do because the actions of characters are not necessary, i.e., deducible from previous actions. But a character's actions will not be arbitrary either. Unexpected actions will occur, this is what hold's the reader's interest, but they will 'make sense' in terms of the situations and the various other personalities in the story. Likewise, the...understanding of God as rational encourages a search for order in nature, but an order that is not necessary. Rather it is contingent, that is, dependent on the action of a wise God who could have created a quite different but orderly universe.[2]

The one word that sums up this situation is the word 'contingent'. We live in an open contingent universe, not a closed and necessary one. It would seem that modern sub-atomic physics has abandoned closed, mechanical systems, and talks of what it calls the factors of chance or even chaos. But we should not simply equate these with irrationality or disorder; as Einstein put it: "God doesn't play dice." The Hebrew god is neither a gambler nor an arbitrary despot, but, as it were, a constitutional monarch bound entirely by a rational and moral constitution within which his freedom operates.

The picture emerging is more that of an 'open' system, a finite universe, exhibiting a subtle interplay between law and circumstance, being and becoming, necessity and chance. Creation is constantly surprising us, showing an astonishing capacity for development and change which gives rise to ever richer patterns of order. For Christians this is immensely important, for they believe that although the world has been given a measure of autonomy by God, it is nevertheless open to his creative activity. If we lose sight of this, we are in danger of lapsing into idolatry – the attempt to make something *within* the world final and ultimate, and to bow down and worship it.[3]

This element of freedom therefore doesn't destroy rationality, order and stability, but rather it serves to enrich these. Science then is both *possible* because of the consistent rationality of the universe, and *essential* because of the contingency and freedom also built into it.

Similarly religions have long worked with the concept of miracle, which is quite different from that of the magic that occurs in the encapsulated cosmos. Miracle represents another form of contingency or openness, but there is nothing either arbitrary or mechanical about it. It represents the understandable intentions of divine providence, and so it is still within the area of the rational. Thus miracle doesn't arbitrarily destroy the order of nature but enriches it. As long ago as St. Augustine, this view was well put:

> Among the pagans, miracle or portent had been understood as the sudden and violent interruption of what was otherwise a regular order, occasioned by the intervention of supernatural powers desirous of signifying pleasure or annoyance. For Augustine, on the other hand, miracle, so far from representing a violation of nature, is simply the (humanly speaking) obscure and incomprehensible in nature. 'Nature', he says, 'is all order and all miracle, but the miracle is the order, and greater than any miracle performed by man is man himself.'[4]

Similarly, in discussing Judaism, Max Weber is emphatic on the almost total absence of magic from the Jewish scriptures, and the restrained use of miracle:

> The miracle springs from meaningful, understandable intentions and reactions of the godhead and its place...in the scripture of the Old Testament generally, is comparable to that of no other holy book...In the absence of magic all questioning of the why of events, of destiny and fate was pushed in the direction of belief in providence, toward the conception of a god who mysteriously though ultimately understandably governed the world and guided the destinies of his people...Unlike the Indian karma, the rational providence of the personal god determined destiny in Israel, [despite the fact that] the masses in need are always out for emergency aid through magic or saviors.[5]

Neither the tribal nor the Axial cosmologies offered this combination of rationality and contingency for the development of science. In the tribal worldviews the full implementation of the microcosmic principle in relation to the macrocosmic provided a kind of rationale that maintained a unitive, closed universe, or else the arbitrary actions of the gods and spirits introduced an element of contingency into everything. There was no marriage between the two principles.

The Axial group also presents an ultimate Reality lacking the qualities needed for this view of the world. It depreciates the world itself as of low value, ephemeral, unreal and meaningless, or worse still, as disorderly, hostile, or positively evil – the realm of darkness and death. The Axial dualist attempts to solve the problems of the encapsulated universe have created worse problems.

The Hebrew duality model therefore offers a coherent system within which freedom and rational order are combined. Instead of Aristotle's impersonal Prime Mover, Hebrew cosmology would seem to require a fully personal 'Prime Caller', who freely calls forth an orderly creation by speaking the word, and who calls forth a response by another word in the garden: "Adam, where art thou?"

A De-sacralized Universe

This feature of contingency and openness in the relation between the world and divinity belongs to what we have called the de-sacralized world. There is a whole range of terms found in use here. In this new understanding the universe is also called 'de-animized', 'de-magicized', 'disenchanted', 'de-mystified', 'de-mythologized' and even (in its proper sense) 'secularized', or 'profane' used as the correlative of 'sacred'. All these terms refer to the same process. I shall continue to use the term 'de-sacralized' as indicating this process most clearly.

In the two millennia BCE, these historical processes proceeded, as all thinking does, by sorting out the varied contents of the original encapsulated cosmos, where nature, humans and the gods are all-in-together. As all thinking does, distinctions were made between these various contents, and the divine was separated from the other dimensions, understood more deeply, and developed in the modes either of the refined, somewhat abstract, dualistic Axial faiths, or in the personalized, duality mode of the Hebrews. It might be said that the divine was more fully and distinctively sacralized to the extent that the other contents, nature and humanity, were de-sacralized. I shall first examine how the Hebrews re-envisaged the realm of nature, and I shall examine it in the three dimensions that are important for science – in terms of matter, time and space.

De-sacralizing Matter Without Depreciation

The two Hebrew accounts of creation in Genesis chs. 1-2 agree in distinguishing the material world from its divine Creator. In the first account there is no suggestion that it is an emanation from the divine, or generated by the god, or fabricated from some pre-existing matter that might have mystic or sacral properties. The world is simply created by divine fiat – God speaks at each stage of creation and that level comes into being. His "spoken word does not *correspond* to the world, does not *represent* the world, is not *symbolic* of the world, but rather *creates* the world. Yahweh's speech calls the world forth...Here clearly is a 'picture' of God who is not a spectator contemplating the eternal logos but rather a God whose words *are deeds*...the notion of word and deed or event are closely linked."[6] This is literally absolute creation, *ex nihilo*, out of nothing, and therefore able to express both the rationality and the freedom of its creator, unhindered by any other factors.

This whole world of nature is placed under the stewardship of the man and the woman, who are not themselves divinities, but only in the likeness or image of God. There is no sacrality built into any part of the created universe. On the other hand there is no suggestion of a dualist inferiority for any part – each stage is described as 'good'.

In the second more poetic account we have more detail about the creation of the man. The 'dust of the ground' that has already been created is good enough to figure as one of the constituents, in its partnership with 'the breath of life' breathed into it by God. We can call this a duality of matter and spirit, without any dualist suggestions of incongruity or opposition between them. And the earth component is shown to be neither mystical nor sacral by the very fact that it has to be complemented by the spirit.

And then, when the creation of humans has been completed by the making of the woman, they are placed in a beautiful garden with its fruit-bearing trees and its four rivers, and they are told they will have to manage it. There is nothing magical or enchanted or sacred about the Garden of Eden, so that it might manage itself under its own powers. While in the next chapter the management becomes very hard work, this is not due to any defect in the garden, nor does it represent any dualist downgrading. It is still a very good portion of the world, given its own nature and function, but caught up in the misbehaviour of its managers.

In these splendid and profound narratives we have a model that represents the whole of Hebrew history. They are an earthy people, living not in great cities, but close to nature, describing it in loving detail, and constantly praising God for the wonders of his creation. There is almost nothing of the ascetic world-rejecting tradition so prominent in dualist religions.

In fact its sacred scriptures provide "the first literary monument of the ancient world...that fully knows romantic love." I am quoting from Samuel Terrien's study of the Song of Songs, with its wonderful title: *Till the Heart Sings; a Biblical Theology of Manhood and Womanhood*. Here the romantic love between a man and a maid is depicted with its sexual expressions without anything suggesting the sex manuals of ancient India or the modern West, much less finding a model in the sexual goings-on of the gods that we have already depicted. The Jewish and Christian faiths have produced their suspicious or negative views of sexuality, but these cannot claim warrant from the Hebrew scriptures. The Song of Songs is firmly entrenched in the canon of the Hebrew Bible. Sex, including its physicality, is a good gift of God, and there is no suspicious or ascetic attitude towards it.

Likewise the promised land 'flowing with milk and honey', prosperous farms and herds, material wealth, physical health and longevity are further good gifts. There was nothing ascetic in the sense of world-renouncing or withdrawal from the world in the Hebrew ethic, and wealth was appreciated provided it was not gained by or used for the exploitation of the poor. The eighth century prophets' diatribes against the rich and powerful applied at this point, and were not a condemnation of wealth and prosperity as such.

In none of these natural benefits is there any suggestion of mystic or magic powers transcending human abilities, and akin to the powers of the gods and spirits, as a kind of independent sacrality. In that era and that area magic is well known and no doubt often resorted to by the Israelite populace. But throughout the Scriptures it is frowned upon. Nature itself has no such powers, and magic cannot be employed to make the crops grow or to manipulate divine favours. As Max Weber pointed out, even miracles affecting the physical world, which might be confused with magic, are rare in the Hebrew scriptures.

A similar attitude resides in the strong prohibition of graven images, of idols. The divine is not to be embodied in this intimate way with any physical thing. The book of Isaiah can mock the idol-carvers of other faiths, with their images made from ordinary blocks of wood, with the shavings heating the bread ovens, and the finished image unable even to walk! There is nothing sacral about these pieces of matter, either before or after their formation as images.

One of the most dramatic and least recognized examples of Hebrew fascination with the wonders of nature is the long account of the crocodile in the Book of Job. Did you know there was such a passage? Read it in a modern translation: Job ch.40: 15-24, and ch.41:7-34, especially in the New English Bible. Older versions separated these two passages, and were uncertain what to call the creature involved – whether behemoth, leviathan, the elephant, or the hippopotamus. And they placed another leviathan, which is really the whale, in between the sections describing the crocodile. No wonder we have missed out on this marvellous account. The NEB settled for the crocodile, which makes full sense.

In the preceding two chapters Job is directed to reflect upon the wonders of God's handiwork in nature – in the heavens and the earth and in its living creatures – the lion, the horse, the ostrich and the eagle, and then in ch. 41 the whale. But it is the crocodile that receives no fewer than 38 verses, with a description that is both imaginative and poetic yet recognisably factual, or zoological.

Now the significant thing is that the crocodile is sufficiently large, ugly, dangerous, fearsome and unknown, sufficiently transcendent of human life, for it to be deified as a demi-god, or set up as a totem, or guardian spirit, or even as an ancestor (with a myth story attached), or else demonized as an evil power. In various tribal cultures one can see it being prayed and sacrificed to, featured in placatory rituals, imbued with some kind of mystic sacral power. But there is no sign of this at all in Job's account. The crocodile may be beyond all human fabrication or understanding but it remains simply a wonderful creature of God. The material of nature remains de-sacralized, ready for scientific study when the time arrives.

De-sacralized Time Becomes Historical

Likewise the understanding of time is transformed; it is de-sacralized in a way that prepares it for its place in scientific procedures. In the encapsulated cosmos it goes something like this: the decisive creative events lay in the past. Then the divine powers, acting through the great culture heroes like Maui of the Maori, set up the world and its occupants and gave people the basic skills of hunting, or fishing, or farming, or of making canoes, or huts, or fire, and the basic social structures and guidelines for living. All this is conveyed in the great body of myth-stories and re-enacted in the sacred rituals. The great reference points, the norms of the tribe, lie in the primeval, creative period of the beginnings. Human welfare depends on constantly drawing on these primeval vitalities, renewing the power and correcting any aberrations from the original patterns. This is how the world hangs together.

In many tribal societies it is believed that life runs down each year, is used up, worn out, corrupted with evils. It needs replacing with new life from the primeval time of the origins. The present time resembles non-re-chargeable batteries which have to be discarded and replaced, or to packaged items like films or foods labelled 'Not to be used beyond a certain date'. There is little concern for the times in between the present and the primeval period – there is nothing reliable or of special significance there any more than there is in the present. Likewise the main interest in the future time is that it should conserve the patterns of the past, that it should deliver more of the same, and so prove acceptable and safe.

The various New Year renewal rituals of tribal and other peoples operate with this cyclic view of time, and they often include a ritual discarding of the old year. A vivid example lies in the rites for the annual renewing of the basic gift of fire; the old, tired fires are ritually put out and the new strong, pure fire is ritually kindled in whatever way it was when the gods first gave it, in the golden age of the past.

Even though there is no escape from this cycle of events there is a sense in which the primal annual renewal provided confidence as a form of salvation from the ills of life. There was none of this when the Greek poet and philosopher of history, Hesiod (fl. ca. 800 BCE), developed his epic poem, *Works and Days*. He presented life as degenerating through Five Ages, from the golden age when the race was as gods and the earth produced rich harvests in Elysium or the Isles of the Blessed, through the silver, copper, heroic Homeric races or ages to the present degenerate iron age; for relief from this he can recommend only hard work!

Even the great civilizations of the Axial faiths and the contemporary Greek philosophers failed to escape from this pessimistic view, from the 'treadmill of time'. So it was that Socrates could envisage repeating the same debates in future cycles, and be haunted again and again by Xanthippe, the same shrew of a wife, and be drinking the hemlock all over again...and again. Here time is seen:

as an enemy, a destroyer, the grim reaper who...swept down all before

Time In Tribal Cultures

THE MYTHICAL VIEW, REPETITIVE, 'CLOSED'

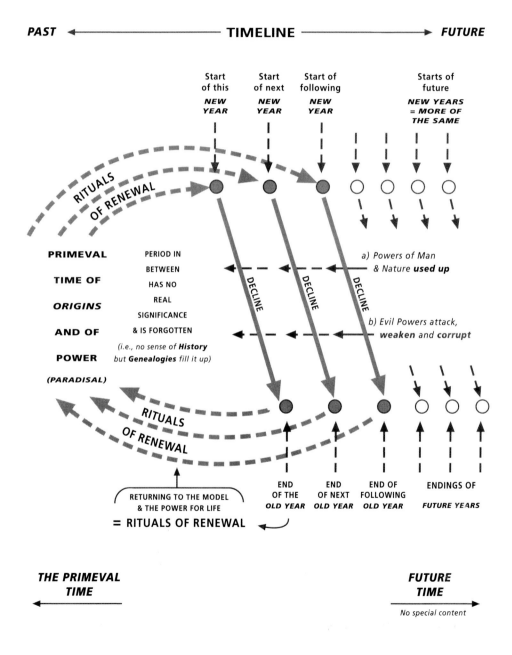

PAST ←————————— TIMELINE —————————→ *FUTURE*

Start of this / Start of next / Start of following / Starts of future
NEW YEAR / **NEW YEAR** / **NEW YEAR** / **NEW YEARS = MORE OF THE SAME**

RITUALS OF RENEWAL

PRIMEVAL TIME OF ORIGINS AND OF POWER *(PARADISAL)*

PERIOD IN BETWEEN HAS NO REAL SIGNIFICANCE & IS FORGOTTEN
(i.e., no sense of History but Genealogies fill it up)

a) Powers of Man & Nature **used up**

DECLINE / DECLINE / DECLINE

b) Evil Powers attack, **weaken** and **corrupt**

RITUALS OF RENEWAL

RETURNING TO THE MODEL & THE POWER FOR LIFE

END OF THE **OLD YEAR** / END OF NEXT **OLD YEAR** / END OF FOLLOWING **OLD YEAR** / ENDINGS OF **FUTURE YEARS**

= RITUALS OF RENEWAL

THE PRIMEVAL TIME ←

FUTURE TIME →
No special content

67

it...Time was negative. As Aristotle said: 'We do not say that we have learnt (anything) or that anything is made new or beautiful, by the mere lapse of time, for we regard time itself as destroying rather than producing...' Hence all reality which was subject to time, i.e., history itself, runs downhill. It suffers degradation and is in a state of decay.[7]

Despite all the anticipations of science in Aristotle and so many others, this view of time would alone be sufficient to rule out future scientific development. Science cannot operate in terms first of a golden age when alone time was sacred, powerful and meaningful, and then in terms of a present time that is of a quite different order, at best meaningless and at worst, harmful. Nor can it operate when the glorious past and the doleful present are linked in cyclic systems of recoveries, whether these be set in the short terms of the tribal year or in the sophisticated calculations of the great civilizations that hugely enlarged the periods of time embraced in these cycles. Time must be a uniform matrix within which all the processes of both nature and of history can operate and be measured.

As against these outlooks the Hebrew view was quite startling, a concept

which has remained practically unique in all of religious history. The God of ancient Israel primarily has to do with the course of human history, and in so far as he can be defined at all it is in terms of history... God is the One who brought the people of Israel out of Egypt, delivered them from slavery and led them into a new land. The events in...which they were successively involved in that land, continued to be the chief manifestation of the reality of God to them...When we compare the Old Testament with the Holy Scriptures of post-Axial religions outside the Judaeo-Christian stream, we find it unique in the attention it gives to human history. Indeed, it contains first-class historiography which is centuries older than that of the Greek historians. The reason for this is that the history of the human race upon the earth, rather than some divine events in a projected other world and rather even than the cyclic processes of nature, constituted the real concern of the God of Israel.[8]

Nowhere is the switch from the cyclic to the linear historical view of time seen more clearly than in the way the Hebrews reinterpreted their three ancient, nature harvest festivals. As a pastoral people, they celebrated the lambing festival each spring, with the annual cycle of the seasons. Here they gave thanks to the gods and ensued the further fertility of the herds. Then, through being especially associated with the time of the year when they escaped from Egyptian slavery, it became a celebration not of natural processes but of this particular historical event. And so it is still in Jewry, the annual Passover festival, with the ritual details all reinterpreted to refer to some aspect of this critical event in their history.

Likewise, after the Hebrews had adopted the agricultural ways of the Canaanites, the midsummer wheat harvest was shorn of its nature fertility motifs and became the feast of Pentecost, a commemoration of the historical revelation to Moses on Mt Sinai. And the autumn nature festival of the fruit harvest became the Feast of Tabernacles, reinterpreted to remind of the historical events of the 40 years in the wilderness area, between leaving Egypt and entering into Canaan. The unrepeatable specifics of history had replaced the ever-renewed processes of nature, as the central events to be celebrated in their religion. Time had become historical and particular events had become the new reference points.

But these events themselves did not represent new Golden Ages when mystic or divine powers were especially available. True, they were founding events, but in a new sense. They now stood early in the timeline of God's actions towards Israel; they were added to the memories of what God had done for their ancestors in the time of Abraham; but they had no special sacral power to be regularly drawn upon. God was equally present and active at each successive stage of their history, just as he had been with Abraham. And now they didn't look back to some Garden of Eden paradisal primeval period, but forward to the fulfilment of God's purpose, as he led them towards his Kingdom with its perfect rule and happiness.

And indeed this new forward view of history, set in ordinary non-sacral time, led to incipient versions of a universal history for all nations, going beyond the limits of tribal history. In Genesis chs.10-11 we have an attempt to bring all peoples within the plan of God, from Noah to the present time. "These are the families of the sons of Noah, after their generations, in their nations: and of these were the nations divided in the earth after the flood." (Gen. 10:32.) And in Isaiah ch.49:6 and elsewhere we see Israel under-standing its own history as part of world history – their vocation was to be 'a light to the Gentiles', and so to bring 'salvation unto the end of the earth' – something quite new, set in the future. Indeed the Christian scriptures as a whole represent a history of the universe, from the book of Genesis account of creation 'in the beginning' to its consummation in the 'new heaven and earth' of the final book, The Revelation of St. John.

In this universe the processes of nature and their corporate experiences as a people are now set firmly within the context of history. Historical time has been redeemed from its rejection as in almost all other faiths. It is now treated as the scene of the divine presence and actions, taken seriously as the door to new things in the future, but without being sacralized or given any power of its own. It is a neutral matrix for the relations between nature, humanity and the divine. And as such it provides one of the essential dimensions for science, a uniform timeline within which things can be located and related and measured. To provide this view of time as intimately related to the divine, and yet not itself identified with the powers of the gods as in the encapsulated cosmos, nor placed over against them as with the dualistic Axial faiths, this is one of the unique contributions of the Hebrew people to the possibility of science.

De-sacralized Space and Place

The other basic dimension of science, space, undergoes the same de-sacralizing transformation. In the encapsulated cosmos as also in the Axial faiths, the spatial dimension is sacralized in the form of special places where the divinities are most potently present and operative. All religions have their sacred places, their sacred mountains, springs, rivers, caves, stones or trees. And they all develop special places of worship or ritual, their open-air altars, their shrines, sanctuaries, and temples. These are the special dwelling places of the spirits and the gods, and they form one of the most universal features across the world of religions.

As these sacred places develop in size and acquire complex buildings, the spatial layout of the temples assumes sophisticated symbolic meanings, some of which we have already mentioned. The religion of Israel lacked nothing here. Once it borrowed the building technology, its temple in Jerusalem became almost a normative model for temples anywhere. It had its graded degrees of sanctity from the outer courts to the inner Holy of Holies, the numinous place of the Holy Ark, the dwelling place of God himself, which even the High Priest might enter only once a year. And the Ark, the wooden chest within the inner Holy of Holies behind the curtain, containing the Ten Commandments on the tablets of stone, combined the sacred object and sacred place in one ultimate instance. The story of the Ark related in II Samuel chs. 4-6 provides a classic example; and there was poor Uzzah, who put out his hand to steady the Ark on its journey, and died when he realized he had violated something too holy to be touched (6:6-7). This House of God, the temple later built to house the Ark, was the central reference point in the life of this small nation.

Now the significant thing is that alongside the history of the Jerusalem temple there runs a radical critique of this whole conception of space and place as being specially sacred. This begins even before the temple is built. The prophet Nathan (II Samuel ch.7) dissuades King David from starting the temple building, however mixed his reasons might have been. When David's son Solomon builds the temple his prayer at the dedication ceremony is ambivalent: to God he says, I have built you a house to dwell in, a settled place to abide in for ever. A few breaths later he is confessing that even the heaven of heavens cannot contain God, much less this house that I have built.

This ambivalence persists throughout the history of the temple. It is seen in the conflict between the priests who served it loyally, and the prophets who denounced reliance on its rituals and sacrifices – and sometimes priest and prophet were the same person. Although the temple was more than once destroyed or desecrated it was always faithfully rebuilt. And although the cream of the nation had no temple during their exile in Babylon, and although many lived permanently abroad, dispersed among the nations, the temple remained the focus of their faith. The religion of the Hebrews relied upon sacred space and place, just as with other peoples.

It is all the more remarkable, therefore, that these same Hebrew people were responsible for the greatest revolution in the place of worship that has ever occurred in the history of religions. Their worship was transferred to the synagogue, an entirely non-sacred place and building. Its origins are obscure, but its development during the exile in Babylon when even the ruins of the temple in Jerusalem were inaccessible, is clear enough; and likewise its spread among the Jews dispersed in settlements around the Mediterranean world. This story, and how it both complemented and finally replaced the temple when the latter was destroyed by the Romans, need not detain us here. We are concerned with how the synagogue radically de-sacralized everything sacred connected with the temple.

Instead of one central consecrated structure and place, designed in heaven and regarded as the cosmic 'centre of the world', there are any number of ordinary, secular, unconsecrated places, freely chosen in domestic dwellings or hired halls. Instead of a specialist, hereditary, consecrated priesthood, any 10 male Jews could establish and manage a synagogue. Instead of a high priest there was a rabbi who was essentially a learned layman, a teacher and spiritual guide; he depended on no secret, mystical or professional knowledge. The rabbi as layman represented the de-sacralization of the social order we shall mention in a moment. Indeed, any layman could stand up to expound the law of God through a discourse equivalent to a sermon, as Jesus did once in a synagogue at Capernaum and Paul did in Antioch in Pisidia.

Instead of an elaborate ritual and sacrificial system led by priests, there is a new form of non-sacrificial worship consisting of prayer, praise, scripture reading and exposition, and the education of the congregation about the faith. Since synagogue worship had nothing to do with temple rituals, this education of the laity was no training for a priesthood to conduct rituals; it focused on obedience to the law of God concerning daily life, on ethical conduct and not on ritual.

The very idea of a congregation regularly assembled together within a meeting hall for corporate worship and education of this kind as the regular form of worship is itself a revolution. Other religions that emphasized personal spiritual development or religion as a way of life might produce a particular teacher or spiritual master with a school of disciples, or guilds or monasteries like the Buddhist sangha. The synagogue was unique in being essentially a lay institution applying to the whole life of a people and not to any sect or party or spiritual elite.

The word 'synagogue' itself referred primarily to an assembly of people and not to a building or a place. It is essentially a democratic fellowship of worshippers for prayer, praise and study, and not under the authority of an official trained priesthood. There was no required liturgical language for in the diaspora the local vernacular could be used instead of Hebrew.

Temples kept their worshippers in the outer courts in small groups, or assembled them there together only for the great festivals. They might be admitted only so far into the sacred interior with their offerings, and only the sacred priesthood might finally approach the image of the god. Congregational worship led by laity in an ordinary secular building was a totally new idea in the history of religions.

The synagogue building itself has no one historical architectural form. It is essentially a secular, multi-functional building not designed for one special sacred ritual. Indeed it is more what we would call a community centre. Historically it has been used for public notices, social occasions, weddings, circumcisions, funerals, accommodation for travellers, the schooling of children, parties and even a lolly scramble. It is not (in classic Judaism) a consecrated sacred building and so, strictly speaking, it cannot be desecrated.

This was de-sacralization at the very heart of a religion. It is perhaps the greatest paradigm change in the whole of religious history, running directly against the worldwide stream. The holy House of God had been replaced by a secular house for the holy people of God. This became the Jews' model for later places and structures for worship after the final destruction of their temple by the Romans in CE 70. It was also the model for the later churches and mosques of both Christians and Muslims. I once felt quite at ease as a Presbyterian conducting Methodist worship in a Jewish synagogue building in a town on Long Island near New York. The whole set-up was in a familiar format. I should explain that the Methodist church had been burnt down and the local synagogue was extending its hospitality while it was not in use on the Sunday.

The synagogue also combines the three forms of Hebrew de-sacralization we have surveyed. In its original and traditional forms, it has no sacredness as a holy place, and no religious symbolism in its spatial layout. It has no sacred material objects, no sacred images of divinity, no sacred ark of the Law, no altar, no sacred relics, nothing imbued in itself with mystique or sacred power.[9]

And its forms of worship do not renew contact with the time of the primeval creation; such new festivals or fasts that developed in its worship referred to particular historical events such as the destruction of the temple, Nebuchad-nezzar's siege of Jerusalem, the assassination of the Babylonian governor. The Purim festival still marks the vengeance taken by Mordecai and the Jews on their enemies as in the stories in the book of Esther; and the Hannukah festival commemorates the re-dedication of the temple after its profanation by the

TEMPLE FEATURES	SYNAGOGUE FEATURES
Special consecrated place or building.	Any secular and non-consecrated building.
Gradation of sanctity towards a sanctuary.	No gradation of sanctity within a building.
Sanctuaries as special holy places with altars.	No sanctuaries or altars.
Priestly control, conduct and leadership.	Lay (rabbis) control, conduct and leadership.
Worship occasional, for personal needs and on major communal occasions.	Worship regular for all, on daily, weekly etc., basis and special communal occasions.
Celebrate mythological and natural events.	Celebrate formative historical events.
Observational worship: main ritual acts delegated to specialists – priests.	Participatory, corporate worship by the whole congregation.
Sacrificial offerings and complex rituals.	Non-sacrificial, with simple rituals.
Special education confined to priests.	Education and edification for all.
Community centres for ritual purposes only.	Centres for multiple and secular purposes.

Greeks. Events in historical times were remembered; time itself was not being cyclically renewed from its sacred source by myth and ritual.

The above table sets forth the many layers of contrasts, overlapping with one another, that exist as between the temple form of worship and the new form constituted by the synagogue.

There could not be a greater contrast than that between the regular congregational and participatory form of worship in the synagogue and the occasional, non-congregational delegated form characteristic of the temple or the sacred place across tribal and Axial faiths.

Space, time and matter had all been radically reinterpreted and all three new forms were embodied in the synagogue, along with non-sacral leadership to be described in the next section. The synagogue therefore exemplifies the comprehensive four-dimensional extent of Hebrew de-sacralization. As the central instrument of Jewish life this very concrete, historical institution also has immense significance as the embodiment of the third type of cosmology that we shall follow in its further development.

De-sacralizing Society and Persons

Alongside these revolutionary distinctions between the natural world and the divine, there was a parallel distinction developing between the divine and the human sphere. We have touched upon this in noting that the synagogue's lay rabbi was not a member of a sacred caste or priesthood, supported by the offerings of the worshippers or a share in the sacrifices. Indeed:

> ...until about the fourteenth century, the Jewish rabbis fulfilled their obligations in principle without payment, originally as a 'secondary occupation'. To earn money by working with one's own hands... held for the old rabbis as a maxim. Thus, we meet here as intellectual champions of a religiosity, gainfully employed persons and among them a considerable number of artisans like Paul the tentmaker. Aside from a few beginnings in medieval India we meet this phenomenon here for the first time.[10]

In Hebrew history there are no holy men whom even to touch is to tap into divine power, as a woman once sought such power for healing by touching Jesus' robe. We recall those Maori who were invited to greet the Pope in the traditional 'hongi' manner of pressing the two noses, but who refused because he was "too holy to hongi with"!

No figures from among prophets or kings are promoted to divine status, and even the greatest of them are depicted with 'warts and all', as only too human. The kings of Israel were sacred only in the sense that they were anointed by God; but they were not divine kings as sole intermediaries between heaven and earth. God even warned Israel against introducing the kingship system, and when they did get it there were the prophets ready to cut kings down to size, and call them to accountability. It is true that the 'divine right of kings' did emerge again in Europe's Christendom periods with 'Holy Roman Emperors', and lasted till monarchs were executed in England in the 17th century and in France in the 18th. But the roots of the critique had long lain fallow within the Hebraic component of Western culture.

Likewise there were no divinely ordained social structures of nobles, of higher and lower castes or classes, and even slaves and foreigners were treated as fully human creatures of God. The model for the ideal or most respected

Israelite was not found as it was in the Axial religions – in the philosopher-kings of Plato, in the Hindu sadhu or holy man, in the Buddhist monk or Zen master, or in the learned sages of China. Indeed Amos, the prophet-shepherd from Tekoa, is extolled, and the ideal Israelite is closer to the peaceful or devout peasant or shepherd. Even the much-praised great king David began life as a boy-minder of the flocks.

In this further social dimension of de-sacralization we might find the roots of later democratic and humanitarian societies, but we shall be following through on the significance for science of the comprehensive de-sacralization of the natural realm. But there is one final comment about this process that is of the utmost importance. At every point it was what might be called a positive de-sacralization, in contrast to the negative de-sacralizations of the dualist Axial Age faiths. The newly secularized realms were never depreciated as inferior, problematic, or as opposed to the spiritual and the divine. Rather were they appreciated in their own created nature as never before. The new cosmology reveals a *biblical duality*, but never an *Axial dualism*. In this distinction lay the kernel of the world cultural revolution the Hebrew people had unwittingly initiated.

The Hebrew Revolution in History

No one of course foresaw the world consequences of this general paradigm change, and its crucial significance for something called science, of which the Hebrews were in total ignorance. The historian and sociologist Max Weber (1864-1920), made massive studies of the religions of China, India and of *Ancient Judaism*; without thinking especially of science, and lacking the extensive resources for its history we are using in this work, Weber came to a similar conclusion about the place of the Hebrew people in world history:

> ...in considering the conditions of Jewry's evolution, we stand at a turning point of the whole cultural development of the West and the Middle East...Jewish religion has world-historical consequences.[11]

These consequences are many and varied, but in focusing on the world-view or cosmology that de-sacralized the scientific dimensions of space, time and matter without depreciating them we have begun to show the roots of the science that has indeed made a world impact and marked the opening of a new era. In this way we are supplementing Weber's judgment by dealing with a crucial area beyond his scope.

We have set forth how the synagogue both exemplified and symbolized the new worldview paradigm. It should be noted that it was not the product of any one thinker, genius or innovator, of the kind we have named as marking the history of scientific beginnings in Greece. Much less did it derive simply from the eighth century to mid-millennium prophets who are overloaded with responsibilities for Israel's religion when this is classed among the Axial faiths. It was not planned or promoted at any one point in their history, although it was clearly encouraged by the emergency situation of the exile in Babylon, and in the Jewish dispersion after the second destruction of their temple by Rome in CE 70.

Nor did the synagogue become a conscious rival to the temple for there was a synagogue within the temple precincts before the latter's destruction, and Jesus and Paul operated within both temple and synagogue. Nor was it ideologically motivated by political or economic reasons, in search of power or even as a strategy for survival; the Hebrews were a powerless people and these changes set them against the stream of the great powers, faiths and cultures, and prevented them from simply merging into the urban landscape.

These changes seem to have emerged in a great variety of circumstances as long drawn-out processes that proceeded somewhat independently, without keeping in step. The de-sacralization of matter may have appeared early, when the nomadic and migrating Hebrews had no permanent territory for the development of sacred places. The de-sacralization of time may well be associated with the exodus under Moses from slavery in Egypt, that became the founding event of the nation and the central feature of so much later liturgical development that celebrated 'the God who brought us out of Egypt.' The de-sacralization of space and place, although anticipated early in their history and even before the construction of the temple, seems to have come last of all, and to have been almost imposed by circumstances. Overall we can therefore see the process as a differential de-sacralization. However this may be, it remains without ordinary historical explanation. There were no obvious historical factors producing, directing and unifying this untidy but profound and long drawn-out, complex process.

To understand all this is nothing less than the problem of the whole Jewish people in history. I am satisfied that the answer lies not in the categories of the historian, but in those of the theologian. The Hebrews themselves would agree with this, for they were the last to attribute these great changes to their own virtues, as a holy or sacred people with special spiritual gifts. National histories glorify their own past; biblical history constantly confesses their failure as a renegade people, and glorifies the God who made something of these historical nobodies in spite of themselves and their repeated disobedience. Their own explanation is theological. But in this exercise we have enough to do in setting forth the historical course of these diverse cosmologies. We must return to their further history and especially to what we shall now call the Judaeo-Christian tradition.

CHAPTER FIVE

Christianity in the Early Centuries

We have now established the three basic options in views of the cosmos – the encapsulated unitive view, where everything is potentially sacral, the dualist Axial view with a negative de-sacralization of the world of nature, and the duality Hebraic view with a form of positive de-sacralization that makes science both possible and necessary.

THE NEW TESTAMENT EVIDENCE

I shall use the same four dimensions of de-sacralization in the Hebrew cosmology for a quick look at what happened in these areas during the early formative period of the new Christian faith that emerged from the Hebrew matrix. Let us look first at the New Testament period.

De-sacralized Places

Jesus and the first Christians still used both temple and synagogue, each in their appropriate ways. Although the silent revolution concerning space and place was underway, and the final replacement of temple by synagogue was only a few decades ahead, in the year CE 70 the New Testament says nothing about buildings for a new Christian community, about churches.

What proves to be significant, however, as a sign of things to come, is the one occasion when Jesus chose a particular building for a special purpose. This was for the last supper with his disciples, and for the institution of what we call the Lord's Supper, the Eucharist, the Holy Communion or the Mass. And he chose the upstairs dining room of an ordinary domestic dwelling.

Despite the sanctity of this rite for the early Christians, it required no sacred place. It may also have coincided with the Passover meal, which had already been re-located in a domestic, non-sacral setting. So even this new important rite instituted no tradition of sacred places. In fact the Christians had to make do with private houses and hired halls for the next three centuries of legal uncertainty and intermittent persecution.

This was possible because a subtle transposition had begun. The physical temple, the building that had served Israel so well, was being transposed into a new personalized, communal form which I call 'Jesus-in-community'. The early Christians were the 'new temple', each of them a stone in the building, with Christ as the corner-stone, and, changing the image, as also the priest, the altar and the sacrifice. God now dwelt in his holy people, not in his holy place. Whatever building was used for meeting was ancillary and utilitarian – just as the synagogue had become for the Jews. And when the Jerusalem temple was finally destroyed, there is no echo of it in the literature of the early church which had moved beyond dependence upon it.[1]

Similarly, as might have been expected, the burial of Jesus gave no rise to a sacred tomb of the founder, as normally with religions. Christianity began without any such holy place of pilgrimage. Interestingly, in February 1995 there was a news report of the discovery of the alleged birthplace of Gotama the Buddha buried beneath a temple in south-west Nepal. If confirmed, this will inevitably become the most holy place of Buddhism; and the news report said the site was already being developed for tourists.

Holy places did later develop in Palestine, and are shown to tourists today. One such is the Church of the Holy Sepulchre claimed to be Jesus' burial place; and there are other similar claims. The establishment of Christian holy sites did not occur until some 300 years after the death of Christ. And then it was not from Christian initiative so much as under imperial patronage, when the emperor Constantine began to embrace the Christian faith.[2] All of which confirms that original Christianity continued the Hebrew de-sacral-

Jerusalem Temple

(SIMPLIFIED SKETCH – HEROD'S TIME)

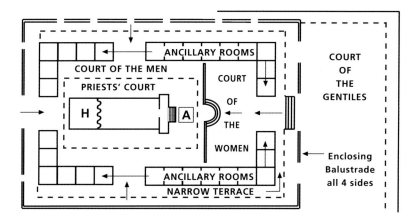

- *Inner holy of holies (H), with sacred objects; High Priest only*
- *Graded sanctity: High priest, priests, men, women, Gentiles*
- *Non-congregational: mainly open courts with outside altar (A)*
- *Symbolic ascents: Mt. Zion site, terrace, steps up to courts*

Capernaum Synagogue

(SIMPLE EARLY TYPE)

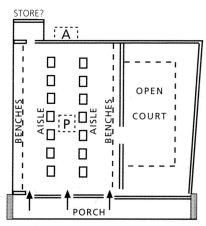

- *Similar to contemporary secular meeting halls*
- *Participatory, congregational assembly on benches*
- *Later added central platform (P) for worship leaders*
- *Later: special 'Ark' cupboard (A) for scriptures*

ization of space and place. There were no holy places. In fact when these did begin, Christian councils discouraged pilgrimages to them, as being pagan practices.

De-sacralized Matter

More briefly, we can confirm a similar Christian attitude to matter. There were no physical sacred relics from Jesus or the disciples, despite those much later claims for the shroud of Turin as Jesus' burial garment, or for pieces of wood from the cross. There was nothing corresponding to the teeth and other official relics of the Buddha, nor the similar Islamic relics such as a hair from the beard of Muhammad or various of his possessions – all still imbued with their owners' spiritual powers. Christian relics would have revived the encapsulated view of the material world as sacral.

On the other hand, there was no Axial Age type of dualism, depreciating the natural world. Jesus' parables and teaching are full of delight in the world of nature as part of God's blessings. This attitude towards the physical is carried over into the acceptance of the bodily resurrection of Jesus; the body with the spirit is integral to the whole person; it is not to be sloughed off or merely resuscitated – in some renewed form it has an essential part to play in the future.

Similarly, this future is envisaged in the last book of the New Testament, in the physical image of a renewed or glorified city, the new Jerusalem, with its streets of gold. In all this early Christianity continued the Hebrew outlook by steering between the dualist separation of the sacred from the material, and the too close identification of these as in the tribal cosmologies.

De-sacralized Time and Persons

Nor was there any re-sacralization of time. The Jewish historical festivals were continued, and the further events were not mythologized – they remained historical events, and played their part in a forward-looking outlook that anticipated the historical return of Christ and the consummation of the Kingdom of God.

Nor again was there any re-sacralization of human beings or communities. In the saying about rendering to Caesar what belongs to Caesar and to God what belongs to God, Jesus was de-divinizing the Roman view of the emperor as divine; and similarly, by implication other later rulers accorded divine status, such as Herod Agrippa who consequently came to such an unpleasant end in Acts 12:22-23.

Jesus himself and the first disciples were artisans, fisherfolk and a bureaucrat – nothing about priestly or saintly status, The 'sainting' of Peter and Paul and the disciples and New Testament writers came much later. Likewise, the Christian communities themselves are described in the New Testament in all their weaknesses, 'with warts and all'. Anything else would have been out of character with the overall emphasis of a Judaeo-Christian cosmology.

A brief theological comment may be allowed here to point out that each dimension of de-sacralization was essential for the Christian understanding of the incarnation of God in Jesus of Nazareth. Here spirit and matter were given equal emphasis, in a duality without a dualism. A real entry of God into this world had to include entry into its material content without divinizing it. If it was to apply to the whole human race, then it could not be tied to a few sacred places inaccessible to the vast majority, nor to one privileged sacred race or nation; nor to one special time of a mythical culture hero not linked in to the normal processes of history. Only a de-sacralized time, space, matter and society could serve for a real incarnation into the world.

The Third Non-Axial Option

At its foundation, therefore, Christianity shared fully in the remarkable, and distinctive features of the Hebrew outlook. Consequently it is the greatest mistake to class Hebrew religion and the subsequent Judaism and Christianity in the Axial group. This places them in opposition to the history of science, instead of in an essential relationship to this history, as I have shown. This is the mistake that many make, and I shall have to follow through on the consequences of this initial misjudgment.

In the first millennium BCE there were three options, not two. As a result of placing Judaism and hence Christianity in the Axial Age group, the Christian position is interpreted as essentially dualist, and therefore is placed over against that of science, both in history and still more so today.

As we pursue the actual history further, into the first 16 centuries of the Common Era, we shall find abundant confirmation of our interpretation. This history has been absent from most popular accounts of religion and science, and it includes some figures whose work is only now being recovered and used. As we examine these earlier centuries, we shall find how erroneous this anti-science stereotype is, and how it still operates both in the popular media and in many of our educational systems.

THE EARLY CHRISTIAN FATHERS

In the last three centuries BCE, the Jews had been increasingly drawn into the world of international Greek culture, and Jewish thinkers had tried to come to terms with it. But in their own continuing de-sacralization of matter, time and space there was no sense that the foundations of science were being further extended. Likewise, in the early Christian period that followed on, it was only as the new faith came to grapple with the Graeco-Roman worldview in succeeding centuries that these issues came explicitly into Christian consciousness.

The fuller implications for a de-sacralized cosmos and the duality option were more clearly revealed when they clashed with the reigning Greek dualist views. And so we proceed to the little-known story of the relations between early Christian thinking and such science as had emerged from the Greeks.

I shall have to be content with the briefest of quotations from some of the Christian theologians and philosophers over the first five centuries CE, who are collectively known as the 'early Christian fathers', and hence this era as the 'Patristic period'. Together they represent an immense intellectual effort to express the Gospel in their contemporary thought world, and to do so with the kind of rigour we expect today in scientific thought. They must be seen in debate with the influences particularly of both Plato and Aristotle, and I shall concentrate on the issues concerned with the physical world that are more obviously those of the sciences.

Clement of Rome (end of first century CE)

I start with Clement of Rome, about the end of the first century of the Common Era. He accepted a good deal of Greek mathematics and astronomy, including belief that the earth was spherical. In this he had broken from the popular biblical three-decker universe of a domed starry firmament above like a tent or a curtain, and a flat earth beneath, standing on pillars in a watery abyss under the earth. But unlike Aristotle, for him the earth was not eternal and it was sharply distinguished from the divine. He referred to "The Father and

Maker of the whole world"; both the heavens and the earth were created, i.e., not eternal, and they were orderly: "the sun, the moon and the dancing stars...circle in harmony within the bounds assigned to them." The whole creation was under the command of one God, and it was a blessing from him – it was good, in contrast to all Axial dualist depreciations.

One astonishing reference in Clement would seem to apply to New Zealanders or Australians. On the basis of a spherical earth, he spoke of people of the antipodes, literally 'those with feet opposite'. He regarded this as an unknown part of the world, separated from his regions by great oceans, with which he never envisaged any communication. But this is the point. He asserted that "the ocean which is impassible for men, and the worlds beyond it (i.e., the antipodes) are directed by the same ordinances of the Master." Even if his Mediterranean world could not know anything about the antipodes, this area was still created by the same God and under his same laws.

That there is only one universe and one set of laws throughout it, is a basic scientific axiom; Clement established it on the basis of his biblical theology. In all these ways Clement maintained the views of creation in the book of Genesis; he married them without difficulty to the permanent contributions of Greek science; and he contradicted the Greek errors.

Athenagoras (late second century CE)

Later in the next century Athenagoras, a teacher in Alexandria, defined Christians as those who "distinguish God from matter...for the Deity is uncreated and eternal...while matter is created and perishable." But this was no dualist depreciation of the material world, for God "gave its harmony, and strikes its notes", as "an instrument in tune and moving in well-measured time." Here we have the Hebrew duality without dualism, the same Creator of a good world with its inbuilt, consistent, 'well-measured' order, a world that science can study and understand. Athenagoras was of sufficient stature to address some of his writings to the emperors Marcus Aurelius and Commodus.

Tertullian (CE ca. 155-after 220)

A skilled lawyer, Tertullian is included here for several reasons: he was an adult convert in CE 193, he was the first substantial theologian to write in

Latin, and he was an effective apologist against the dualist Gnostic sects and philosophers who formed the chief danger to early Christianity. Thus he asserted that the eclipses of the sun and moon proved that such changeable bodies could not, as with most of the Greeks, be divinities, for these were by nature eternal and changeless.

He affirmed the reality and goodness of the material world (contra dualisms and Gnosticism) by proving that Christ was really born, lived and died in human flesh with a real human nature, so much so that he was in fact ugly! And his resurrection from the dead provided the basis for the Christian confidence in the resurrection of the body in some form, one of the most powerful beliefs expressing a positive and non-dualist attitude towards the material world; although a difficult doctrine, especially for philosophers and the contemporary mind, always being re-examined but always maintained.

Since Tertullian's main theological concerns were with Christology and the Trinity rather than with the doctrine of creation, his treatment of cosmological matters shows how these could not be avoided as the early Christian thinkers wrestled with the Greek thought world surrounding them.

Clement of Alexandria (CE ca. 150-ca. 212)

A century later than Clement of Rome, another Clement founded a school of Christian teaching in Alexandria. He was quite familiar with the great cosmological system of his fellow-Alexandrian, the great Greek astronomer, Ptolemy, much of which he took for granted. Likewise he recognized fragments of truth in earlier Greek philosophers such as Pythagoras whom he quotes as affirming that "God is one; and he is not...outside the universal order, but within it...the supervisor of all creation...the wielder of His own powers, the light of all His works in heaven and the Father of all things."[3]

This cosmology was seen in allegorical relationship to the tabernacle of Moses in the wilderness period of Israel's history, and at one point the lamp which stood by the incense-altar is seen as representing a heliocentric universe:

> By it were shown the motions of the seven planets, that perform their
> revolutions towards the south. For three branches rose on either side of
> the lamp, and lights on them; since also the sun, like the lamp, set in

the midst of all the planets dispenses with a kind of divine music the light to those above and those below.[4]

One might read too much into such imaginative statements were it not that Clement breaks from Greek cosmology at several other important points, such as the divinity of the blind forces of nature or of the heavenly bodies.

Why, pray, do you infect life with idols, imagining wind, air, fire, earth ...this world itself to be gods? Why babble in high-flowing language about the divinity of the wandering stars...through this much vaunted – I will not call it astronomy, – but astrology.

And again:

Let none of you worship the sun; rather let him yearn for the maker of the sun.[5]

To make the latter distinction was well in advance of the persistent astrological element in most cosmology, for even Christian thinkers maintained something of this confusion about astrology as a form of divine revelation, right up to the time of Kepler.

Origen (CE 185-254)

Half a century later again we listen to Origen, an immensely influential Egyptian theological teacher, first as Clement's successor at Alexandria and then at Caesarea. He too was emphatic in seeing the created material world as good, despite its ugly and evil aspects that did suggest a dualist or negative view. It was created out of nothing by an eternal, rational, and transcendent deity who gave it a systematic order or structure that enabled us to comprehend it, and who stood in a relation to the world quite different from that of Aristotle's Unmoved Mover.

But much of his writing was devoted to the dimension of time. He took Greek ideas so seriously that he attempted a Christian version of the cyclic view of history. But he could not accept an eternal and purposeless recycling, a blind treadmill. Even the cyclic movement must have had a beginning and must lead to the fulfilment of God's purpose for creation.

...the major steps of redemption culminating in Christ...in their uniqueness barred any possible flirtation with the idea of eternal and purposeless
cosmic cycles. 'For if it is said that there is to be a world similar in all
respects to the present world, then it will happen that Adam and Eve
will again do what they did before, there will be another flood, the same
Moses will once more lead a people...out of Egypt, Judas will also twice
betray his Lord, Saul will a second time keep the clothes of those who
are stoning Stephen, and we shall say that every deed done in this life
must be done again.'[6]

It was quite inconceivable that Jesus should be born again in Bethlehem,
should live and be crucified and rise from the dead, over and over and over
again. So he envisaged each cycle, including the cycle that included the
incarnation in Jesus, as serving a special purpose and leading to further
development, almost as if in a spiral structure. Here we have an ingenious
but unsuccessful attempt to marry the cyclic and the linear views of time.
Its significance is that it should have been made at all, in an attempt to
escape the confines of an eternal return cosmology.

In similar fashion, Origen attempted to incorporate the Greek beliefs
that the sun, moon and stars were endowed with life and intelligence. But
whereas the Greeks saw them as divinities, Origen pointed out that they
could not be divine and therefore perfect, because they underwent changes
like other earthly things, and because in the scriptures they received
commands from God. So he saw them as created beings, the agents of God.
This was the first and critical, even if only partial, step in de-sacralizing
them. Once again, we see the Christian thinkers maintaining their anchorage
in the Judaeo-Christian cosmology while speculating on how to employ the
Greek cultural framework.

Lactantius (CE ca. 240-ca. 320)

The variations in these speculations is seen in Lactantius early in the fourth
century. He was an adult convert to Christianity, a distinguished Latin writer
who was tutor to the emperor Constantine's son. He turned Origen's argument
right round: the heavenly bodies could not be animate, because their movements showed no variation – anything living would not act like a fixed
machine. Christian speculation could try every avenue.

But he was no friend of New Zealanders or Australians. He contradicted Clement of Rome: it was nonsense to think the earth was spherical and that the antipodes existed. There couldn't be "people whose footprints were higher than their heads", or that "rain and snow...fall upwards upon the earth". So much for some of us. But again, here was Christian speculation at work on cosmologies.

Athanasius (CE ca. 295-373)

Another Alexandrian, Athanasius, became the key figure in the fourth century theological debates about the relation of the human and the divine in the person of Jesus that took shape at the first general council of the Church, at Nicaea in 325.

It was vital for the future of Christianity that an incarnation embracing both the real humanity and the real divinity should be affirmed, as against the heretical view of Arius, an Alexandrian priest who taught a Gnostic view of the Trinity. Here the Father, the Son and the Holy Spirit were three separate essences; only the Father as fully God was eternal, and the other two had been created by God in time, and so were divine only in a derivative way. If Jesus was not God incarnate then the central claims of the Gospel about what God had done in Jesus were undermined; however exalted, he was only a created, time-bound, human figure after all, with no ultimate authority.

This was another form of the classic Greek dualism of time and eternity, with rationality existing only in the latter. On this view there could be no science in the sense of rational understanding of the material and temporal world, which was both irrational and ephemeral. It seems a far cry to link up the possibility of science with the debates at Nicaea, and with Athanasius' victory over Arius, but nothing less than a worldview or cosmology was at stake. This was confirmed at the Council of Chalcedon in 451 and we shall examine some of its further contributions below.

For Athanasius and the Council of Nicaea, the divine and the human, the heavenly realm and this world, were not opposed to or separated from one another. In fact they inter-penetrated without losing their distinctive identity; how to describe this was the problem and our diagram of the three cosmologies is one attempt at representing the issues. For this purpose Athanasius developed his doctrine of inter-penetration in the form of co-inherence, described in the Greek term 'perichoresis', with its suggestion of three equal figures dancing linked in a circle – perichoresis is now a technical term in recent revived study of the Trinity.

Here we have another version of what I have called the duality view, as against a dualism. It has immense significance for later scientific thinking, not only as providing the worldview necessary for science, but as a first formulation of the ideas about interacting fields of force that emerged from Faraday and James Clerk Maxwell in the 19th century and formed the basis of post-Newtonian physics – a kind of co-inherence within the structure of the physical world, parallel to that within the godhead.

Basil the Great (ca. 330-379)

Basil 'the Great' was a Greek theologian in the fourth century in Cappadocia, a Hellenized culture area in the east of Asia Minor. He was also a practical organiser of churches and monasteries, indeed of what is sometimes regarded as a most important event in the history of medicine – "history's first hospital open to the public on a regular basis."[7] The further influence of Basil's hospital will be mentioned when we come to the Arabic contributions to medical science.

Being highly educated, he knew a good deal of Greek science and he gathered a number of these issues together under a Christian critique, sometimes in very specific and homely ways. Thus he pointed out that the Greek identification of the circle with the divine and the eternal because of its endless nature, might be true in imagination but not in practice. To draw or make a circle one had to begin and finish somewhere. Circles, like the created world, had a beginning and an end, and had no divine or eternal mystique about them.

This was further shown by a child's spinning top, which moves in circles although it is rotating not in the heavens, but upon the earth. The heavenly bodies and the earth were all of a piece, made of the same materials, earth, air, fire and water. On earth these elements are the same as in the heavens, and in both areas they behave in the same way.

This contradicted the Aristotelian division of the universe into an imperfect, corruptible, sub-lunar world extending out to the orbit of the moon, in contrast to the eternal, incorruptible, perfect region of the heavens lying beyond the moon's orbit. For Basil the whole universe was of the same

Typical Greek Geocentric Cosmos

PYTHAGORAS HAD 9 CONCENTRIC SPHERES; ARISTOTLE, 55

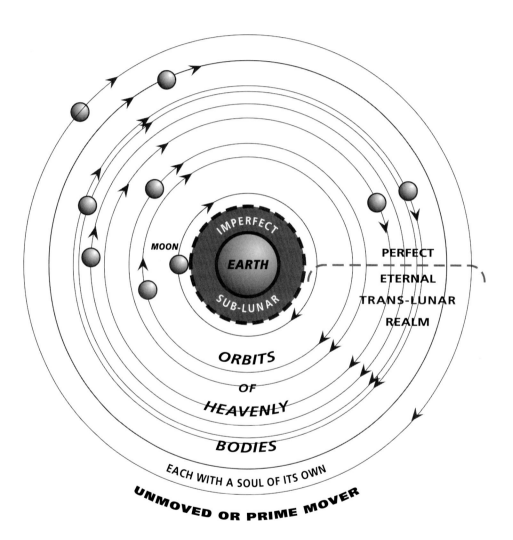

DIVISION INTO PERFECT AND IMPERFECT REALMS

materials and under the same laws of its Creator; another basic scientific axiom.

He also questioned the Aristotelian view that the Prime Mover, or else the divine spirits in the heavenly bodies, must continue imparting motion directly to everything that moves. Again he was watching the child's top, and he puts it this way: "Like tops, which after the first impulse, continue their revolutions, turning upon themselves when once fixed in their centre; thus nature, receiving the impulse of this first command, follows without interruption the course of the ages..."[8] Otherwise Aristotle's Prime Mover would be like those entertainers who spin plates on the tops of thin wands, and who have to keep running round giving a fresh twirl to each plate as it slows down! Basil's spinning top provides an early formulation of the idea of impetus, that can be traced back to incipient beginnings in Jewish thinkers in the second century BCE.

Basil found the principle of impetus in his theology of creation; in Genesis God had directly created the different sections over the six days, but on the seventh he rested and left the created world to get on with it according to the laws he had built into it; he didn't have to keep jostling it along, giving each part a further twirl. This is an early understanding of the relative autonomy of nature, of its distinction from its creator. It may be the child's twist of the fingers with the top, and the commands or laws of God with the created world, but in each case the effect continues indefinitely after the initial action. This allows for the principle of the conservation of momentum (here in its angular form), or of inertia, that will appear repeatedly in Christian thinkers over the next 12 centuries. Finally it replaces the false physics of Aristotle, and in the hands of Descartes, Galileo and Newton makes modern physics possible.

Basic in Basil's view was the creation of the universe out of nothing, by divine fiat, and its being given a relative autonomy and the orderly form we discover and express in the laws of nature. In these ways it is contingent upon and represents the freedom and rationality of its creator. This was quite unintelligible and foreign to the Greek mind, where the universe was of divine nature, eternally co-existing with God, and therefore was necessarily what it was, rather than contingent upon God or anything else at all. Basil was gathering up views we have found developing over the centuries since Clement of Rome. He rooted them in the Book of Genesis, and his study, the *Hexaemeron* (the six days in Genesis 1), influenced works with similar titles up to the 12th century which were consolidating this essential for the existence of science.

Before leaving Basil, there is one area where he used his acceptance of aspects of Greek cosmology in a way that people in the antipodes can appreciate. He recognized that there were stars about the south pole of the spherical earth that he could never see from his region. He might not have known the name of the Southern Cross, but he seems to have been allowing for it. Thank you Basil!

Augustine (354-430)

Outside the New Testament writers, Augustine, who spans the end of the fourth century Common Era, is the dominant thinker in the first thousand years of Christian history. Born in what is now Algeria, he was in later life long-time bishop of Hippo, near ancient Carthage in Algeria. Here we can give only the briefest of references, where his manifold thinking touches our theme.

Inevitably we start with his early career as a philosophy teacher, a pagan like his father, despite his saintly Christian mother, Monica. Then for nine years he became a convert to a religion that had developed out of Zoroastrianism in Persia, to Manichaeism, an extreme form of dualism. Mani, its founder, claimed to be the redeemer of the human soul, which belonged to the realm of the light, but was entangled here in the darkness of the evil, material world. Release was to be effected by an ascetic and celibate life on the part of the élites.

When Augustine found the Manichaean teachers couldn't answer his philosophic questions, he dropped out and turned to neo-Platonism, although this was really a more refined form of dualism.

The story of his Christian conversion at the age of 32 was told later in the famous *Confessions*. His interests leaned more to human spirituality and psychology than to the sciences, although he did include some important scientific issues. The universe, being the creation of God, was not eternal but finite in space and time. Time itself had its created beginning, and history served the purposes of God. The notion of cyclic returns was ridiculous, and eliminated any possibility of happiness; who could be happy facing such a dreary personal prospect of going through it all, over and over again?

And who could take the Christian gospel seriously if it meant a salvation that came and went interminably?

Augustine had urgent practical reasons for developing the philosophy of history and therefore of time, that occupied his later life and was expressed in one of the great books of Western culture, *The City of God*. What was anyone to make of the patent collapse of the great Graeco-Roman culture and the Roman empire? The northern barbarian tribes had been eroding the empire's boundaries; when Augustine was 24 the Visigoths had killed the emperor in battle; in 410 they sacked Rome itself; when he died in 430 another Germanic tribe, the Vandals, were besieging nearby Carthage. The inconceivable was happening around him.

For Augustine, these events could not be part of the predestined cycles of history. So he developed a great philosophy of history wherein they became part of its predestined course towards God's purposes for it. We don't have to commend his use of predestination in order to appreciate his insistence on the linear view of time, despite its horrific current contents for him.

This affirmation of historical time was another and most influential basis for later science as it studied the natural history of the world. Indeed, the sober Christopher Dawson in an essay on 'The City of God' in 1930 claimed that Augustine was not only the founder of the Christian philosophy of history, but actually the first man in the world to discover the meaning of time. His subtle and profound mind found a peculiar attraction in the contemplation of the mystery of time which is essentially bound up with the mystery of being. He was intensely sensitive to the pathos of mutability. "For all this most fair order of things truly good will pass away when its measures are accomplished, and they have their morning and their evening."[9]

His other great contribution is to affirm of the world that 'a good God made it good.' This condemns all dualisms, even though his own ascetic personal style continued throughout his life. He is to be quoted on this:

I must admit, I am unable to see why mice and frogs have been created, or flies and worms for that matter. I see, however, that all things, in their own way are beautiful...I cannot look at the body...of any living creature without finding [and listen to this!] measure, number and order...Look for the craftsman...one other than the One in whom there are supreme measure, supreme numericity, and supreme order...He arranged everything according to measure, number and weight.[10]

He finds the flies and the worms a problem, but beyond this he is in fact recognizing some of the basic categories of physical science in the created world ('measure, number and weight'), as part of its given order. He also affirms the importance of scientific knowledge in its own right. Let him speak again, in words immediately applicable today:

> It is often the case that a non-Christian happens to know something with absolute certainty and through experimental evidence about the earth, sky and other elements of this world, about the motion and rotation, and even about the sizes and distances of stars...about the nature of animals, fruits, stones and the like. It is...deplorable...that he should hear a Christian give, so to speak, a 'Christian account' of these things full of laughable errors.[11]

A pretty good warning, is it not? – especially for the current 'Creation Science' Christians. Science must have its own autonomy. And if it proves the earth to be a sphere, as Augustine believed with the Greeks, and if the Bible talks of the heavens as like a tent above an apparently flat earth, then the Bible must be interpreted so as not to contradict what is clearly true in science. But note that he is even more concerned about the authority of the Bible in its proper domain, as the medium of the true knowledge of God and of eternal happiness.

For Augustine, there are a lot of things the sciences didn't tell him; he was, for instance, still unsure as to whether the stars were alive or not. If they were, they might influence natural phenomena such as the tides and the seasons, but not human lives. Here he quoted the observation of the different lives of twins, even though they had the same horoscopes. He quotes one he knows, an army officer, with a wife and children, continually in conflict; his twin sister lived the peaceful life of a holy virgin. So astrology was rejected. And besides the uncertainties of science, he says, there is much that we don't need to know for our salvation. Biblical knowledge doesn't depend on these things. And this, perhaps, remains part of a pragmatic working model for the relation of science and religion.

I hope it will not appear as a debunking of a great mind if I succumb to the temptation to report on one subject where he seems to have abandoned his own wisdom. It concerns the controversial subject of those people at the antipodes. And it appears that Augustine used the Bible, rather than astronomical or geographical evidence, to prove that people like these could not exist! There may be some excuse for him insofar as the force of gravity was then unknown, but this common ignorance only makes the openness of those Church Fathers who did allow for life at the antipodes all the more remarkable.

Boethius (ca. 480-524)

This immensely learned and high-minded patrician held senior administrative and political office in Rome in an unstable period and represents one of the last of the 'Fathers' of the Church. From the influence of his extensive writings I select only two features.

First, he was largely responsible for the curriculum of the later mediaeval studies being divided into the three literary arts (the 'trivium') and the four mathematical sciences (the 'quadrivium') – arithmetic, geometry, music (theory, mathematically analysed) and astronomy. He began a translation programme of the Greek classics in these areas, for very little of Aristotle, Plato, etc., was available in Latin; this began to prepare the ground for the invasion into Western Europe of Greek-Islamic culture through the Arabs in the 12th and 13th centuries.

Secondly, his worldview, despite his Greek learning, was deeply Christian, as in this sample from his great hymn to the Creator:

> O Thou, that dost the world in lasting order guide,
> Father of heaven and earth, Who makest time swiftly slide,
> And, standing still Thyself, yet fram'st all moving laws,
> Who to Thy work wert moved by no external cause:
> But by a sweet desire, where envy hath no place,
> Thy goodness moving Thee to give each thing his grace,
> Thou dost all creature's forms from highest patterns take,
> From Thy fair mind the world fair like Thyself doth make.[12]

This, in English translation, comes from his *The Consolation of Philosophy*, and has the added poignancy of showing a calm faith, although he was writing in prison while awaiting his political execution by an emperor who followed the heretic Arius. Here the world is seen, and the place of human beings in it, in rational, moral and beneficent terms, and while Boethius uses philosophic reasoning more than biblical or theological sources to establish his divine providence, it was a Christian cosmology in operation.

His *Consolation* and other works were so widely distributed in the mediaeval period that "From Boethius's textbooks, the Middle Ages...learned to conceive of nature as an ordered whole and to deal with it rationally."[13] As we shall see below it was this often unrecognized aspect of mediaeval thought that Alfred North Whitehead brought to such wide attention in 1925 and demolished the popular stereotype.

Boethius' worldview was one version of the cosmology that emerged from the centuries of struggles between the Christian Fathers and the Graeco-Roman milieu, and it set the scene for the delayed developments of science in the later Middle Ages. A much fuller version was developed by the last of the Fathers we include in this survey, who suffered the contrary fate of total neglect.

John Philoponus (ca. 490-ca. 566)

The relation between science and the Christian religion in the first half millennium of our era is gathered up and confirmed by one man in the sixth century, John Philoponus (i.e., 'John the workaholic') who has been seriously neglected in discussions of the history of both science and theology. He has been called a 'sixth century Archimedes in philosophy'; I am prepared to regard him as not only the greatest theoretical physicist in antiquity, but the greatest before Isaac Newton.

He was nevertheless lost sight of within a century of his death, only to be discovered late in the mediaeval period, and to have inexplicably faded from view for the second time early in the modern scientific period. Of the truly great figures in the history of science, the irony is that he seems to be one of the least known.

Individual scholars, however, have been rediscovering Philoponus, and his significance for the physical sciences. In 1983, 75 Philoponus scholars from many disciplines met in conference in London, and initiated a translations programme to make available in English all his extant works, from the original Greek and from Syriac and Arabic versions.[14]

Now who was this Philoponus? He was a Greek Christian, a first-class lay scholar, professor of philosophy in the Academy in Alexandria, which had possibly been brought into the Christian faith by St. Mark of the Gospels. Now it was the second city in the empire after Rome, and the greatest Jewish city in the world. It was the home of learning both Greek and Jewish, the place where the Hebrew scriptures had been translated into Greek (the Septuagint), where Philo, the greatest Jewish philosopher in antiquity, taught at the turn of the millennium, where Athanasius had been bishop, with a famous library, and a lighthouse that was one of the seven wonders of the ancient world.

Philoponus was at the heart of Graeco-Roman culture, with a rich inheritance indeed, and has been called 'the most learned man of his time'. It was after his death that Alexandria was captured by the Persians in 616, and then by the Arabs in 646. Through them its literary treasures were transported east, away from Europe to the Arab centres of learning, the ancient Damascus and later the new Baghdad; here they were translated from the Greek first into Syriac and then into Arabic, and so lost to the Latin scholars of the West for some seven centuries.

Theologically, he had the misfortune to belong to the Alexandrians, who subtly disputed the Council of Chalcedon decisions about the two natures of Christ. The Byzantian establishment simply did not understand the developing meanings being given to basic terms like 'nature' both in theology and in physics, and especially by Philoponus; they were still seeing through the dualistic spectacles of Plato and Aristotle He was formally condemned (as 'monophysite', supporting one nature only) in 680, and also charged with tritheism; this, together with the fall of Alexandria, explains his subsequent neglect. He was, however, certainly a convinced and orthodox trinitarian with a Hebraic, biblical cosmology, and we are concerned with the implications of his cosmology for his science. Here he exhibited the method of scientific experiment and observation that would have corrected much Greek science had he not been lost for nearly a thousand years.

First of all, he was one of the greatest exponents of Aristotle in antiquity, with commentaries on almost all his works, and he adopted much of Aristotle's system for the orderly classification of nature. Although there were other and pagan critics of Aristotle, Philoponus was the first to mount such a devastating critique of the deductive method and much of the content of Aristotle's physics and cosmology – there was no rival to its thoroughness until Galileo.

Much of his work amounted to the sort of basic 'paradigm change' that T.S. Kuhn finds at critical points in the history of science. Here I can but summarize his main critiques, and indicate their Hebraic source and their profound scientific significance.

Aristotle's cosmology was attacked at three connected points:

1. The heavenly bodies were not divine and animated beings, but were parts of God's creation, and made of the same stuff as this world – earth, air, fire and water, the four basic elements common to much of Greek science. The light of the stars derived from their fiery state, and it was the same as that of glow-worms and luminescent fish; de-sacralization indeed! And astrology was rejected as pagan, and as immoral since it destroyed freedom of the will.

2. In the same vein, the heavenly bodies were not perfect. They did not move with regularity in the perfect shape of the circle, nor in a series of concentric spheres – a series of 55 of these was needed by Aristotle to account for all the movements! On the contrary, some star movements were irregular, and the planets moved in directions opposite to that of the stars, and not always in perfect circles – a simple matter of observation, as against Aristotle's *a priori* deductions and postulated aether.

3. Likewise, the apparent changelessness of the universe, especially the heavens, does not mean that it is eternal, ungenerated and uncreated as in most Greek thought. Change in such immense bodies in the heavens can be invisibly slow. And look at Mt Olympus, he said; it shows no signs of growing or diminishing, but no one says it is eternal. In any case the universe was created by God *ex nihilo*, out of nothing. Accordingly, in God's purposes it had a beginning and it will have an end, with much change in between. In short, the heavenly regions were not divine, not perfect, and not eternal. Until this is accepted there can be no real scientific study of them. Philoponus' views threw the whole beautiful system of the great Ptolemy into disarray, by undermining its basic assumptions.

While Aristotle's physics was almost universally accepted at a great many points, and by Philoponus also, where there was conscious conflict with a Christian position he rejected Aristotle in the many ways that led into modern science. Three in particular may be summarized:

1. For Aristotle, the motion of anything required both a continuous motive force and a resistance that had to be overcome. Since there would be no resistance in a vacuum, movement there would become instantaneous, with an infinite velocity. But this is inconceivable, so a vacuum is impossible; even God could not make one. To this, Philoponus presented long and ingenious criticisms supporting the vacuum, which were substantially correct.

2. Aristotle asserted that heavier bodies fall faster than lighter ones, and that their speeds were proportional to their weights. Philoponus seems to have actually tried it out experimentally, something Aristotle didn't do. Listen to Philoponus: "Our view may be corroborated by actual observation more effectively than by any sort of verbal argument." And so he decided that, no matter how different the weights, they hit the ground "at practically the same time." This is important for the correct theory of gravity, which Aristotle could never have reached.

In our culture the popular story is that it was Galileo who first reached this conclusion, after dropping weights from the leaning tower of Pisa. It now seems there is no substance to the tower story, and, more importantly, that Philoponus was a thousand years before him with the correct theory, and further, that Galileo had read Philoponus on this subject. But don't expect the Pisa tourist office today to tell this to the tourists who think they are at the site of a great scientific breakthrough.[15]

3. The third critique of Aristotle's physics is vitally important. Recall that his theory of motion required two factors – a force continuously applied to the moving object, and a resistance to be overcome, as from the air through which it moves. In a quite fanciful way Aristotle asserted that the air displaced at the front of, say, an arrow, rushes back alongside it to prevent a vacuum developing behind it, and then turns round and pushes the arrow from behind, as part of the motive force. Philoponus mocks it: "such a view is quite incredible and borders on the fantastic." Fantastic it was, indeed!

In place of this, he proposes a theory of impetus whereby the thrower of an object imparts a non-material dynamic power to the object itself, and this force, being now internal to the object, keeps it moving indefinitely, if there is no resistance. "Could the sun, moon and the stars," he asks, "not be given by God, their Creator, a certain kinetic force in the same way as heavy and light things were given their trend to move...?"[16]

This places the heavenly bodies and earthly phenomena under the same laws, and abandons the dualism between them. Even more importantly, it is the forerunner of the later theories of inertia and momentum that are embedded in Newton's first law of motion, which represents the basis of physics. Moving bodies keep moving in a straight line unless something interferes.

Philoponus applied a similar dynamic theory to the movement of light. Aristotle offered a static theory whereby light was the actualizing of something transparent, there all the time but potentially illuminating in the form of light. By contrast, Philoponus regarded it as a form of motion, with a kind of impetus imparted by the Creator to the luminous body and travelling with a practically infinite velocity. This radically new kinetic theory of viewed light was analogous to his new impetus theory in the behaviour of matter, and together they amounted to a rejection of Aristotelian physics and mechanics. Even more remarkable is their anticipation of the unification of impetus and light theory by James Clerk Maxwell in the 19th century that provided the basis for Einstein and modern physics, and to which we refer further in chapter 12.

But what has this to do with Hebraic cosmology? It is virtually the same theory of impetus that Basil of Cappadocia had enunciated two centuries earlier in more theological terms – that God set his creation moving with its own laws and did not have to keep jostling it along, like the stage plate-spinner. These early Christians might have been expected to replace Aristotle's Prime Mover with bands of angel plate-spinners, busily engaged in keeping everything moving. But at least their thinkers didn't do so.

Now hear Philoponus himself on this: God, having finished the creation of the universe, "hands over to nature the generation of the elements one out of another, and the generation of the rest out of the elements."[17] That sounds like a summary of the evolution of the universe from basic materials that modern cosmology and physics could identify with. The relative autonomy of nature, with its own order and laws, is basic to science, and these early Christian thinkers were laying the foundations. And yet even the historian of science, Herbert Butterfield, speaks of Christian thinkers challenging the Aristotelian theory of motion "as far back as the fourteenth century", ignoring Philoponus in the sixth and Basil the Great in the fourth century![18]

Among the Church Fathers with whose cosmology Philoponus agrees at so many points, he stands out as also a philosopher and scientist. In this way he represents the value of philosophical and scientific thought freely pursuing truth without explicit theological controls, whether Christian or Greek, although the basic implicit positions of a Christian worldview are still fruitfully at work. We shall explore this cross-fertilization further in chapter 12; for the present we employ T.F. Torrance's summary:

> As a realist scientist and theologian, John Philoponus was...concerned with dynamic reality, not with abstract or philosophical investigations [like much of Aristotle]. By his own astonishing achievements, even in some respects anticipating Clerk Maxwell and Einstein, John Philoponus showed us...that a proper theologian can be a good scientist, and that a good scientist can be a good theologian, concerned to develop not only the internal role of Christian theology in science, but actually to contribute innovative advances in a scientific understanding of the created order which natural science could not do on its own.[19]

It is good to report that, after some 13 centuries, the anathema against Philoponus has been lifted by the Greek Orthodox Church, through the instigation, I understand, of Professor Torrance.

Qualifications

At this point I must protect myself against charges of cooking the historical evidence by a biased selection of thinkers, or of sections of their works. Thus Boethius whom we have been examining, when it comes to his discussions of the Trinity uses the familiar Greek term of 'substance' as applying to the three internal Persons within the Trinity, and does not improve matters when he goes on to define a 'person' as a 'rational, individual substance'.

This atomistic and rationalist view has caused endless trouble and prevails in much modern Western culture, as over against the co-inherence inter-relational views we have already emphasized as applying to personal relations, whether within the godhead or between human persons. The Fathers had not got it all worked out in completely consistent ways but by and large they had developed a massive and drastic alternative to the reigning worldviews of their milieu.

I am also aware that Greek thinkers before and after the time of Socrates and the advent of Aristotle anticipated many of these ideas about cosmology, and had a more inductive approach. Thus Anaxagoras in the fifth century BCE examined a meteorite and concluded that the heavenly bodies could not be divine or animated beings, but were made of stone just like the earth. But these potentially fruitful early Greek ideas were overridden by the triumph of Platonic and Aristotelian more deductive philosophies that re-divinized the heavenly spheres.

There were also Christian thinkers who disagreed with those we have examined. Some accepted the reigning Aristotelian positions, just as most of the Christian world accepted and used Ptolemy's astronomical system right up to the 16th century, often without any special interest in cosmology. These included names that were notable in some other important respects. Thus Theodore (born ca. 428), Bishop of Mopsuestia in Cilicia, held to Aristotle's belief that the stars were kept in motion by the angels. Jerome (ca. 345-419), the translator of the Bible into Latin, denied the concept of the antipodes, and on biblical grounds regarded Jerusalem as the centre of the earth and therefore of the universe.

Others like him simply ignored scientific knowledge, and based all the knowledge needed on the Bible, either literally or allegorically interpreted. Thus Cosmas, an Egyptian monk (fl. 6th c.) noted that Moses had been told to design his tabernacle sanctuary in the desert period on the model of the heavenly sanctuary. Therefore the structure of the universe could be deduced from what was declared about the tabernacle in the Book of Exodus and in the Letter to the Hebrews. A complex cosmology was then set forth, of which the following description by H.P. Nebelsick provides a sample:

> The earth, like the table of the shewbread, is rectilinear; its wavy border signifies the ocean which surrounds the earth. The walls of the tabernacle simulate the four walls of heaven; and the roof shaped like a half cylinder, portrays the vault of heaven. The firmament...forms the floor of the upper storey and the ceiling of the lower storey...the place where angels and human kind dwell. The upper storey is the kingdom of heaven to which Christ...had ascended...The sun, moon and stars are carried along below the firmament by angels who are also in charge of the air, the clouds, and diverse phenomena.[20]

And there will always be such among us, but they contribute nothing to science and little if anything to theology. But those I have chosen to expound in brief, and others who could join them, are both influential and representative of where Christian thought was going in these areas. This is shown by the decisions of the great ecumenical councils of these early centuries. The interesting fact is that while they were dealing ostensibly with domestic and central theological matters, and not with scientific issues, nevertheless their decisions had the profoundest importance for the future of science. This, of course, is because all truth ultimately is interconnected as one.

Ecumenical Councils and Creeds: Chalcedon (451)

I shall end this section with a very different epistemological contribution to science from a creed drawn up by the Council of Chalcedon in 451, in northern Asia Minor, more or less opposite the then Constantinople. It sought further understanding of this great problem – how Jesus could be both divine and yet also really human? Neither then nor since has Chalcedon satisfied everybody, but it has not been replaced by something better.

Now I am not going into its concepts, but rather into its methodology, and the implications for an epistemology of science. What it did was systematically to rule out the four common unsatisfactory solutions to the problem, always a useful start on any issue. And it did this by drawing up a set of four guidelines for all thinking on the matter.

Each guideline ruled out one of the common false solutions. I don't need to detail these four heresies here, for the guidelines have their own importance and speak for themselves. Chalcedon said we must face the problem of Jesus having both a human and a divine nature – and these are its own words: (1) without confusing the two natures; (2) without transmuting one nature into the other; (3) without dividing them into two separate categories; and (4) without contrasting them according to either area or function.

Now I suggest that we have here a theory of knowledge, not only about the relation between these two concepts, the human and the divine, but about the relations between all concepts and so about everything in the universe. All thinking and understanding involve spelling out the relationships between this and that, between A and B, or whatever. And in all thinking we must not confuse the terms with one another, nor simply turn one into the other (what we call reductionism), nor separate them from each other, nor consider either in less than its wholeness and its proper functioning (overtones of the holistic principle). In other words, we must retain the integrity both of A and B, and of their relationship; we must take the data seriously and never manipulate or 'cook' it. This is the Chalcedonian method.[21]

Surely the procedure here laid down for theological enquiry is a procedure for any field of enquiry. It arose in seeking to understand the relations between the two categories of the human and the divine, exemplified in Jesus; it equally applies in studying the relations within the members of the Trinity – the same four warnings; and it applies to the way the sciences treat the relationships within their data.

I don't see how it could be improved upon. Ultimately all sciences, natural, human and divine, share a common methodology at this point. And there's a thought; the procedures of these ancient bearded theologians at Chalcedon were in fact defining the procedures followed in the science departments of the modern university.

Some will find this derivation and formulation of a general epistemology from an ancient Christian Creed rather preposterous, wherever mind-set and assumptions do not allow for such a procedure. I could produce a theological argument to show why I should not have been surprised when this application of Chalcedon first dawned upon me. But I will be content with drawing attention to a very similar account of relationships and their epistemology from a quite different source as to time and discipline. Michael Polanyi's discussion of the interface between adjacent levels in his Hierarchy of Being presents each level as following its own laws or principles, and none can be understood without reference to its adjacent levels, nor be reduced to any form of the other levels. This translates very readily into the Chalcedonian formulation, and Polanyi produces it as a physical scientist and not as a theologian. And if all truth is one, then why should the similarity be a cause of surprise?[22]

It is almost a fashion in some sophisticated quarters to make snide and dismissive remarks about ancient and argumentative theologians and their creeds; a favourite is the alleged 'hair-splitting' over the difference of one vowel between words like 'homoousia' (of the same substance) and 'homoiousia' (of similar substance), and of this difference being important. The fact that the two adjectives differ by only one vowel is entirely accidental and can be important in any language. The difference here, of course, goes right to the heart of this basic theological issue, as we have pointed out in connection with Athanasius above.

One popular parody ignores the contrast I have been presenting, and speaks of a synthesis of Greek and Hebrew ideas of God. Then, 'if that were not complex enough', it refers to the three Persons in one substance, and quotes the same section I have noted, but mocks it as merely a "verbal conundrum"..."a maze of abstract philosophical terms" which it was no wonder "a substantial minority rejected."[23]

It is a great pity to find the Chalcedonian guidelines pilloried like this. They are really so logical, as philosophical terms so simple, so common-sensical, and they are honoured daily in modern science.

Antecedents and Achievements

At this point I must again recognize that many of these differences from Aristotle and the Platonists, so well developed by Philoponus and others, had occurred earlier in Greek thinkers. There were the Pythagoreans two centuries before Aristotle, with their ideas of the earth demoted from its fixed centrality and floating as one planet among others around a central fire. There was the Greek philosopher Epicurus, a generation younger than Aristotle, who propounded the notion of a vacuum, of space as a void with physical atoms moving around in it. But he still regarded this spatial universe as infinite and eternal.

And many others might be named as contributing ideas contrary to the ruling Aristotelianism. There was Aristarchus of the same period with his heliocentric universe; and Hipparchus in the second century, who was the greatest astronomical observer in antiquity. He seems to have rejected Aristotle's theory of motion and suggested the idea of impetus. But there is no record of his work, and it had no influence until Philoponus rediscovered the idea seven centuries later and gave it a basis in a Hebraic cosmology.

After this tribute to their predecessors, we may seek some summary of the achievements of the Christian thinkers in these first six centuries of the Common Era. It lies in two areas. Firstly, it presented an answer to the perennial problem of the relation between the one and the many without lapsing into dualism; the duality cosmology preserved both unity and diversity as positive features of a reality that exhibited both rationality and contingency.

Then there is the persistent de-sacralization that they had inherited from their Hebraic ancestors, the de-divinization of the created universe. If this de-sacralization was focussed on the heavens, on astronomy, this was because that was where the Greeks had concentrated, and where it had to be refuted. It was characteristic that one of the greatest and longest lasting achievements of the Greeks was the astronomical system of Ptolemy, accepted universally in the West until the 16th century, and lingering even longer.

This concentration of the Greeks reflected the pervasive dualism in their philosophies. These started with the belief that "perfection was to be found in the static and unchangeable features of the world, because...if a state changes, it either changes for the better or for the worse; perfection cannot change for the better, so any change would mean that it ceased to be perfection. Life lived according to these principles would eventually lead to escape from the limitations of earthly existence..."[24] Putting it another way, and in terms of Aristotle's distinction between the 'form' of anything and its 'matter', the latter was always the inferior dimension.

The life of a gentleman therefore consisted of contemplation and speculation upon the changeless realm of mathematics, and upon its close associate, the next most changeless realm of astronomy. Astronomy and mathematical calculations teamed up together, as the least experimental of the sciences, fit for gentlemen without soiling their hands, or making instruments and experimenting. That sort of involvement in the inferior physical world was fit only for slaves.

It would be quite impossible for the Greeks to imagine Jimmy Carter, a former President of the United States, joining with his hammer in a Habitat work party on a new home for the poor. Even Archimedes, who became famous for experimenting and inventing all sorts of clever mechanical devices, regarded these technical things as beneath the dignity of pure science and declined to leave any written record of them, apart from his treatise on sphere-making and his planetary model – astronomy again![25]

It wasn't that the Greeks were devoid of technology, for we have already listed some of their achievements. It was their negative attitude towards it and its association with manual work that prevented the development of empirical science in Greece as the essential handmaiden of scientific knowledge.

This contrasts strongly with our noting above the Israelite rabbis earning their own living as artisans, with the ideal Israelite being a shepherd or devout peasant, with the many artisans among the first disciples of the carpenter from Nazareth, and with Paul, the chief intellectual expositor of the new Gospel, earning his way along by tent-making.[26]

This attitude running right through the Bible appears in the later Christian monastic principle that 'to labour is to pray', or with one of the founders of Christian monasticism, St. Benedict, who required six hours' manual labour daily from his monks; or with the great development in the practical arts that marked the monasteries, and their contributions to technology – their inventiveness of labour-saving machinery, especially the harnessing of water-power, and the mechanical clock.[27]

It is not surprising then that we see signs of experimenting in people like Philoponus. This derived from the duality cosmology operative throughout these early centuries. Here the world was both good and rationally ordered, had its own laws in the relative autonomy given by its Creator, and was the field of human stewardship and responsibility. So, as we have seen, there was every incentive to explore it systematically in the ways that led to what we know as science, assisted increasingly by technology.

CHAPTER SIX

Europe's Conversion
and the Rise of Islam

Christianity in the 'Great Recession'

Given this favourable cosmology, what happened next? This period used to be known, unfairly, as the 'Dark Ages' in European history, the six centuries after the collapse of the Roman Empire; Latourette called the years 500-950 the period of 'the great recession', and in many respects this term applies.[1] On the other hand, better knowledge of this period reveals a great age of Christian expansion, at least geographically, with the conversion of the Slavs and others in the Balkans and finally of Russia in the east, various barbarians in northern Europe and Scandinavia, and the remarkable missionary activity in northwest Europe of Irish Celtic Christianity. With the important exception of Muslim inroads in the Balkans and Spain, and of barbarian pockets, Europe could in some loose sense be seen as a Christian continent, where the foundations of the two later Christendoms, West and East, were being laid.

It is not our concern here to follow the Christian history of the period, which would take us into the revival of the Roman empire under Charlemagne of the Franks, crowned as Holy Roman Emperor in 800, into the cults of the saints that replaced the local divinities, and especially into the development of the monastic movements that provided a structure for order where the Roman Empire and its cities had collapsed. We must, however, take brief account of the place of this earlier monasticism in the history of science.

The Earlier Monastic Movement

We have already referred to the contribution of the monastic orders to the development of technology as something closely connected with the attitude to work of the religion they professed. For example, from the viewpoint of fundamental importance to science, there was the invention, or at least the widespread use and development, of mechanical clocks in somewhat later monastic history in order to regulate accurately the times of worship through the twentyfour hours.

At their best the monasteries combined a practical interest in the technologies associated with agriculture, apiculture, animal husbandry, and building, with the contemplative life enjoined by the disciplines of the various orders. Each abbey was a self-contained economic organism, like a Roman estate, and we get some idea of its extent from the plans of the St. Gall abbey in Switzerland about 820.

> It is no longer the simple religious community envisaged by the old monastic rules, but a vast complex of buildings, churches, workshops, storehouse, offices, schools and almshouses, housing a whole population of dependents, workers and servants like the temple cities of antiquity. The monastery had in fact taken the place of the moribund city and was to remain the centre of mediaeval culture until the rise of the new type of city in the eleventh and twelfth centuries.[2]

The Greek distinction between the manual and the contemplative life had vanished, and 'the religious', the monks were themselves the workers. The injunction of St Molua (founder of Kyle monastery in the sixth century) to his monks is typical:

> My dearest Brethren, till the earth well and work hard so that you may have a sufficiency of food and drink and clothing. For, where there is sufficiency among the servants of God, then there will be stability, and when there is stability in service, then there will be the religious life. And the end of religious life is life eternal.[3]

This says everything about work and technology, a stable society, Christian worship, and the goal of life. In modern terms this has analogies with the relation between applied and pure science, between knowledge of practical use and knowledge satisfied by the beauty and elegance of the created world, or by solving Fermat's Last Theorem! And of course it totally rejects all dualist cosmologies and represents the combination of theory and practice in a Hebraic duality worldview.

I shall take but one individual example from the monasteries for a contribution in the realms of science that is probably quite unexpected – from a monk known as 'The Venerable Bede', with his *Ecclesiastical History of the English Nation.*

Bede (ca. 672-735)

Bede was a scholarly monk and devout Christian, working within the great monastic developments of his time in Northumbria. Most of his writings were biblical exegesis or historical, including the first history of English Christianity, which is still the major and highly regarded source for this area and era.

It should be remembered that the works of the Greek philosophers and scientists were away in the Islamic east, locked up in Greek, Syriac or Arabic, and unknown to the Latin scholars in the monasteries of the West, where scholarship was being slowly revived. So there was neither means nor incentive to debate the great issues of this world and the heavens with Aristotle and all the others as there had been for the earlier Christian Fathers.

When therefore we read that 'Bede is recognized as the first indigenous scientist of the West' it is not surprising that his scientific activities were of a practical kind and concerned with the measurement of time that was important in the monasteries. Early in life he published on chronology (703), and was still at it with a much enlarged version in 725, which remained a standard work for centuries. His main interest here was with the disputed dates for Easter, related to positions of the moon; Bede derived the name itself from the Anglo-Saxon spring goddess, Eostre, and this has stayed. Here it would be tedious to follow the debate and the cultural and other factors involved, and it is sufficient to note that obviously this enquiry leads straight into mathematics and astronomy, with which Bede became involved.

He was also involved, and in the same enquiry, in a co-operative scheme to monitor the tides along the English coast, and from the astronomical work attached to all these activities he 'gave the first clear statement of the sphericity of the earth in mediaeval times'. He also ventured further afield by leaving out the view that stars were animate beings with souls, held by Isidore, archbishop of Seville (d. 636), when Bede revised Isidore's work a century later.

Bede is therefore presented as marking some of the earliest stages of Western scientific thought that was to await some five centuries for its development through the incursion of Greek-Arabic culture from the east, when the debates of the early Christian Fathers were picked up again.[4]

ISLAM: ACHIEVEMENTS AND IMPASSE

Islamic Achievements

The collapse of the Roman Empire, a period that Latourette called 'the great recession' (a term we have qualified in various ways) was in part due to the invasions of the northern barbarian tribes, and in part to the rise and spread of imperial Islam from the seventh century. Philoponus' Alexandria declined after its capture by Persians, then Arabs, in that century, and its resources were replaced by two new Muslim centres of vast wealth and learning, Damascus and later Baghdad, where the Greek manuscripts were relocated and translated into Arabic or Syriac, often by local Christian scholars equipped in Greek.

Islam was the one great faith that shared in the Judaeo-Christian inheritance, and, along with its eclectic borrowings from the great civilizations and their technologies and wealth, might have been expected to develop its scientific potential still further. This is especially so in view of various contributions that Islam did make, especially to astronomy and to mathematics, where they supplied the Hindu-Arabic system of numerals without which neither science nor mathematics could proceed – imagine handling numbers like 1899 in Roman numerals!

Not having inherited the dualist outlook that depreciated the world, the Arabs were free to link the theoretical world of mathematics, especially of geometry, to the practical realms of art and architecture. And so they later produced those superb buildings and gardens in Spain – the mosque at Cordoba and the Alhambra palace at Granada.

Islam and Medicine

They also made great advances in the art and theory of medicine. It is not commonly realized that Islamic medicine took over a well-established Christian tradition, tracing at least from Basil the Great whose public hospital has already been noted. This was copied by Ephraim of Syria (ca. 306-373) about the same time, with a public infirmary of 300 beds in the Mesopotamian city of Edessa. In the next century Edessa became a medical teaching centre, and when its school was closed by the Byzantine emperor in 489, many teachers moved to the city of Nisibis, also in Mesopotamia, and built up a school there.

Teachers from this school were used by the Persian ruler in the mid-sixth century to establish yet another school, at Jundishapur in southwest Persia. After Islam had conquered the area in the seventh century it was the Christian successors of these schools who were used by the Muslim caliphs to found a hospital and medical school in the new city founded at Baghdad in 762. What is rightly claimed for Islamic medical science must be seen against this little-known background, as well as in relation to the collection and translation into Arabic of the extensive works of the great Greek physician Galen, which was going on at the same time by the highly eclectic Arab scholars, assisted often by Christian scholars.[5]

Only a few indicators of the remarkable sophistication of Arabic medicine can be given here. We cannot do better than quote some of Stanley Jaki's summaries of outstanding individuals:

> ...the greatest figure of Arab medicine, al-Razi (865-925)...the author of *A Treatise on the Small-Pox and Measles*, which...contains the first clear description of the major symptoms of the two diseases and shows its author as a keen observer and respecter of facts...more importantly he wrote the medical encyclopedia, *Kitab al-hawi*, that is, 'Comprehensive Book' which...included the whole of Greek, Syriac and early Arab medical knowledge in addition to ample material from Persian and Indian medical sources...Intensive interest in eye diseases went on into the 14th century... [and even of] trachoma and the description of cancer of the eyelid...[and] a systematic account of the anatomy of the eye...including detailed discussion of some operations, especially the ones connected with cataract.[6]

Congruent in this interest in the eye is the concern with optics, where the Arabs had collected all Greek knowledge by the ninth century and in the tenth took the subject a good deal further. For example, Ibn-al-Haitham (965-1038) extended the laws of refraction from the plane to concave and parabolic surfaces, discovered spherical aberration, located the focus of a paraboloid and the use of the camera obscura, experimented with magnifying glasses and approached close to the modern theory of convex lenses. Theory and practical experimentation were fruitfully combined in this Arab scientist.

Islam and Mathematics

Clearly, mathematics was involved in most of these developments and we take only one sampling from a wide range of mathematicians – the unexpected if somewhat later example of the Persian Muslim, Omar Khayyam (d. early 12th century). His world reputation as a poet dates mainly from his mid-19th century discovery and the English translation of his quatrains as the *Rubaiyat*. In his own day he was better known for the first comprehensive classification of algebraic equations with respect to the number of terms, and for his efforts to correlate algebra with geometry. Algebra, geometry and trigonometry were all advanced by the Arab mathematicians.

Islam: Astrology and Astronomy

The interest in mathematics supported considerable activity in astronomy and astrology, where the Arabs took over a vast body of knowledge from the cultures of India, Persia, Greece, Syria and Egypt. In astrology these peoples had worked out all the possible basic combinations, and there was nothing new to discover. Arab astrologers, however, applied spherical astronomy and exact mathematical methods to the rough calculations of the Greek astrologers and sought to turn astrology into a more exact science.

Their early philosopher al-Kindi (fl. 850) was supported in his astrological work by the popular enthusiasm for astrology ever since it first arrived in Greece in the third century BCE. He took seriously the belief in the various circles of time, from the Great Year down to shorter periods, such as 20 and 240 years, within which the events in Islam's short history might be fitted. The idea that the fate of nations and religions might be governed in this way was exceedingly difficult to accommodate to the ambitions and confident future of Islam, or to the theology of the Qu'ran.

Although astrology has continued as a regular feature of popular Islam – there was a court astrologer in Turkey into the 19th century – increasing knowledge of Greek philosophy supported Arab philosophers in their strong rejection of astrology and in its distinction from astronomy. There had been almost no observational data after the time of Ptolemy and the second century; since Ptolemy himself had included observations made some 270 years earlier by Hipparchus, and since astronomy depends on data over long periods of time, the Arabs had strong incentives to add their own much later and more accurate observations, set out in astronomical tables that were used into the 16th century, along with improved instruments and a more exact terminology.

In these ways in the next three centuries after al-Kindi their leading philosophers extended the scientific quality of astronomy – al-Farabi in the 10th, Avicenna in the 11th, and Averroes in the 12th century. In so doing, they laid the foundations for the European astronomy that, subsequent to Copernicus and the invention of the telescope, was to replace its flowering under the Arabs.

Internal Opposition to Science

On the other side of these advances there was much that was unscientific taken over from Greek philosophers. This included a geocentric universe, which was also intrinsic to astrology, and:

> ...that the spheres and the stars are living beings, rational, operating by their own will; that the spheres have souls which exist in their bodies as our souls in our bodies; and that as our bodies move...towards the ends we have in view, so also do the spheres, which have as their end the serving of God.[7]

Despite this pious conclusion Islamic theologians who expounded the Qu'ran and had no interest in science were extremely hostile to the more free-ranging philosophers influenced by Aristotle and the Greeks. Al-Ghazzali (1058-1111) believed in the independence of religion and the prophetic inspiration in their own right and mounted an attack in his *The Incoherence of the Philosophers*, especially Avicenna. To this, Averroes (1126-98) replied with *The Incoherence of the Incoherence*!

The Arabic scholar best-known in the West today is probably their great historian, Ibn Khaldoun (1332-1406), who resembled Al-Ghazzali in his 'religious' view of religion and based his theory of history on the governing contributions of the dynamic prophet movements. His attitude to physics, the basic science, proved only too true as far as scientific development in Islam was concerned. After brief historical accounts of some of the scientists dealing with physics, he describes it as "the beginning of the motion of bodies – that is, the soul in the different forms in which it appears in human beings, in animals and plants."[8]

This is simple animism, set within the encapsulated cosmology we have critiqued, and Jaki's comment cannot be bettered:

> An anima or soul was not such if it did not have some measure of freedom of action. Now if a star or a stone had a soul, each could conceivably deviate from its predetermined path at any given moment and most unpredictably...there could be no science which is strictly predictive about purely physical motion. In other words, if science was to be born, nature had to be de-animized.[9]

Ibn Khaldoun went even further to doubt the value of physics and all science, for "The problems of physics are of no importance for us in our religious affairs or our livelihoods. Therefore we must leave them alone."[10]

Islam was therefore much more internally divided than Christianity had been in the Christian Fathers we have surveyed, where there was a steady move away from Aristotelianism, supported by a biblical doctrine of creation, and climaxing in Philoponus. And this attitude contrasts strikingly with the place that science was at this same time assuming in the culture of Christian Europe.

Theological Opposition: Allah's Freewill

We may identify two of the basic reasons for the scientific impasse in Islam and its failure to sustain an ongoing scientific development. On the one hand, orthodox Islam so stressed the free will of Allah as to make it absolute, unqualified by the constraints of a rationality shared by both God and humans. Therefore in the world Allah had created there was no place for a rationality that science could comprehend; indeed it was impossible to hold the notion of natural laws that might impose constraints on the infinite power of Allah.

The illustration used was that of the ruler who took daily rides through his capital city along a regular route. But he could vary the route in any way he liked, according to the whim of the moment, and no one could be sure when or where. The relation between God and world was, as it were, too contingent and too free. "Verily Allah will cause to err when he pleases and will direct whom he pleases." (*Qu'ran*, Sura 35, vs. 9).

This is a kind of total predestination, a complete determinism by God. The Creator of the universe cannot endow it with inbuilt laws of its own, for fear of limiting his own power. Without such laws or regularities there is nothing for science to discover. Other names for such a position are voluntarism and occasionalism – by a special voluntary act the Creator is responsible for each occasion, for each 'atom' of existence, whether event or material reality.

Lacking the Theory of Impetus

It is not surprising that thinking Muslims turned away from the Qu'ran to the Greek sciences of their abundant manuscript resources, and took Aristotle on board without reckoning either with their own theologians or with the severe Christian critiques of Greek worldviews made in the preceding centuries.

In particular we note that there was only one Muslim scholar who later raised the possibility of inertial motion and who differed from Aristotle on this – Avicenna early in the 11th century. But he lacked a view of a contingent universe, created *ex nihilo*, that could support the independent impetus idea. He held the very opposite view, a Greek pantheist outlook whereby creation was an emanation from the deity, who eternally and of necessity produces the world. The impetus idea requires a Creator who stands in distinction from a creation operating under its own laws, including this, the first law of motion, which lies at the very basis of science.

It was therefore not sufficient for Islam to inspire a great civilization with wealth and learning and power over such wide territories, where it interacted with and borrowed from so many other cultures; it was not enough to be encouraged by a more linear view of history, to live more freely in a de-sacralized world of nature and worship within such an emphatic monotheism; all these substantial advantages were not enough to develop a genuine and modern science when, as we have seen, the vital element of a properly controlled contingency in creation was lacking.

Arab rule and culture, after its establishment in the eastern Mediterranean areas, moved across north Africa and entered Europe via Sicily, southern Italy and the Iberian peninsula. During the earlier part of this advance, towards the end of the first millennium, Christianity was at a low ebb, while Arab Islamic culture was advancing to its greatest heights. It was therefore a powerful vehicle for the re-introduction into Europe in the early centuries of the second millennium of the Greek science and philosophy that the Christians had lost and that Islam had both preserved and absorbed. And the chief feature of this was the Aristotelianism that was to dominate much of science and theology in the first five centuries of the second millennium that we shall now proceed to survey.

CHAPTER SEVEN

History of Science
in the Middle Ages

I now pick up the history of science in Christian Europe from the end of the first millennium, and use the rather old-fashioned term 'Middle Ages' to cover the period from the 10th to the 16th centuries. Here we still encounter not only ignorance but firmly entrenched stereotypes of the mediaeval period as authoritarian, obscurantist, dominated by a reactionary, corrupt, anti-scientific Catholic Church from which the later Greek-inspired Renaissance and then modern science emancipated us. The scientists were the martyrs and the churchmen were the persecutors. The pop histories of Copernicus and Galileo are still with us, despite their exposure by historians of science as ideological distortions. I doubt if there is any reader who does not harbour at least remnants of some such picture. I was certainly brought up on it.

Whitehead and Duhem

In the English-speaking world perhaps the first person publicly to query this cultural cliché in relation to the history of science was the philosopher-mathematician Alfred North Whitehead, professor of philosophy at Harvard University. In 1925 he gave the Lowell Lectures, later published as *Science and the Modern World*, and the first lecture was on 'The origins of modern science'. Here the establishment received a rude shock from one of their own. Whitehead first agreed with our earlier statements that:

> ...there have been great civilizations in which science...has only fitfully appeared and has produced the feeblest result. For example...China forms the largest volume of civilization which the world has seen. There is no reason to doubt the intrinsic capacity of individual Chinamen [sic] for the pursuit of science. And yet Chinese science is practically negligible. There is no reason to believe that China if left to itself would ever have produced any progress in science. The same may be said of India [and] the Persians.[1]

He went on to declare that "the approach to the scientific mentality which had been attained by the Greeks" was "absolutely in ruins" by the sixth century, and that the "Middle Ages formed one long training of the intellect...in the sense of order", i.e., of rationality in creation. But more than this: "science also needs the instinctive conviction...that there is a secret ...which can be unveiled", based on a confidence "in the intelligible rationality of a personal being", which is "an unconscious derivative from medieval theology." One can imagine the startled silence at such a politically incorrect suggestion. Worse still, his book sold over a million copies in about a decade.

Now Whitehead was far more of a pantheist than an orthodox Christian, so he could hardly be accused of favouring mediaeval theology. Nor was he an historian of science. But he had a French wife with a convent education, and so it is possible that he knew of the one historian who had set forth these ideas on the basis of his own research a generation earlier. This was the distinguished French physicist, philosopher and historian of science, Pierre Duhem, whose death in 1916 had been prominent in British newspapers.

What amounts to the persistent persecution of Duhem by the French scientific establishment is a shameful chapter in the history of science in France. Duhem was an intelligent and devout Catholic and the establishment was ruled by the anti-clericalism then at its height in France. They unjustly failed his first doctoral dissertation and all his life kept him from appointments in Paris, and they frustrated the publication of the second half of his great ten-volume *Le Système du Monde* (on cosmologies from Plato to

Copernicus) till the 1950s, some 40 years after his death – Stanley Jaki (never given to understatement) described this as "the greatest individual work of original scholarship in modern times"!

Duhem is still little known in the English-speaking world but he stands at the beginning of the new discipline of the history of science, which Whitehead so unexpectedly rooted in the Middle Ages. This discipline began to develop with the work of another Frenchman of very different religious stripe, Alexandre Koyré, from the 1920s. In the Anglophone world it was the philosopher Michael Forster's three sophisticated articles in the philosophy journal *Mind* in 1934-36 that provide a classic starting point. He identified the Christian doctrine of creation, our duality cosmology, as the necessary presupposition of science.[2]

Renewed Critiques of the Middle Ages

Since the 1930s there has been a wealth of research and publication, and from this I can pluck only one or two examples of the way Christian thinkers in the Middle Ages continued in the same vein as in the earlier centuries to dispute the reigning Aristotelian physics. I shall focus on the ideas of motion and of impetus that we have already found to the fore in earlier Christian critiques of Aristotle. One of the early and best-known histories is Herbert Butterfield's *The Origins of Modern Science,* in 1949; it is significant that his opening chapter is entitled: 'The historical importance of a theory of impetus.'

The re-introduction of Greek resources to Western Europe occurred through the Arabs and also by the reverse movement of the Crusades and the Christian kingdoms they established in the eastern Mediterranean. Christian thinkers, especially those gathered at the great new universities of Paris and Oxford, had to grapple anew with the Aristotelian worldview, and especially with his theory of motion, embedded as it was in a pagan theology. I select only one example, Jean Buridan, a 14th century professor of philosophy, twice rector of the University of Paris.

Jean Buridan (14th century) and Thomas Bradwardine (d. 1349)

Buridan knew the works of Philoponus and he examined again the belief in "God setting the heavens in motion once and for all by imparting an impetus that would keep them moving indefinitely...Impetus was defined as the quantity of matter in motion times its velocity", and he said there was no need of Aristotle's air currents to keep an object moving. Instead of Basil's spinning top, Buridan used the example of a millwheel that would continue to spin once it was set in motion, and it would do so even if fitted with a close-fitting cover to keep the surrounding air away – the experimental method taking hold again.[3] He also used the example of an athlete on the long jump dropping back so that he could run faster for the start and acquire more impetus. And the athlete feels the air in front resisting him, rather than as Aristotle said, the air behind pushing him! I should let Buridan's own words speak on these matters:

> ...since the Bible does not state that appropriate intelligences move the celestial bodies...it does not appear necessary to posit intelligences of this kind, because...God when he created the world moved each of the celestial orbs as he pleased, and in moving them he impressed in them impetuses which moved them without his having to move them any more...and these impetuses...were not decreased or corrupted afterwards, because there was no inclination of the celestial bodies for other movements...But this I...say...rather tentatively so that I might seek from the theological masters what they might teach me in these matters as to how these things take place.[4]

This clear theory of conserved impetus comes explicitly from Buridan's biblical doctrine of creation. It rejects the Aristotelian need for spiritual movers of the heavenly bodies, or for angels busy at the same task, and it prepares for Newton's first law of motion. Note also how as a layman he recognises the theological authority needed for his cosmology – a philosopher-scientist recognizing the autonomy of theology in its own sphere.

In terms of the two main ideas I have been using, Buridan brought the heavens and the earth under the same laws of motion and so rejected the dualism between them. Then he related this one universe to its creator in an open, contingent fashion. There were many others in these centuries wrestling with the dominant Greek cosmology, attempting to draw on its grand schema while critiquing it at some of these key points on the basis of a non-dualist Christian position.

Distinguished names can be mentioned, of those more directly concerned with this critique and especially with these two ideas:

Robert Grosseteste, Roger Bacon, and Franciscans Peter John Olivi and Francis of Marchia (13th century); in the 14th century, Thomas Bradwardine the mathematician, William of Ockham, Nicole Oresme and Albert of Saxony; and in the 15th century, Nicholas of Cusa and the great Leonardo da Vinci who took up some of Buridan's ideas on impetus – but their mere listing is of limited value.

One of these I will mention very briefly – Thomas Bradwardine the mathematician (d. 1349). His contribution was to forward the process of expressing the behaviour of both the earthly and the heavenly bodies in the same mathematical terms. This abandoned the dualism between the two realms and also developed the essential place of mathematics in defining the laws of nature. But Bradwardine had his precursors, as with Robert Grosseteste a century beforehand, who saw the kind of uniformity in nature that allowed it to be quantified mathematically.

He was also to anticipate one of the bases of Copernicus' thinking two centuries later, "motivated not by empirical data but by the theological belief that a mathematically minded Creator could not have created anything so asymmetrical as Ptolemy's system of celestial motions."[5]

I can now refer back still further to a phrase we quoted in Augustine when he described the creation as arranged according to 'measure, number and weight'. These are quantitative notions, susceptible of mathematical treatment, and they were not original to Augustine. In fact they come from the Hebrew Book of Wisdom, or Wisdom of Solomon, which was recognised as scripture by Greek-speaking Jews, the early church, and remains in the Catholic canon. "Thou hast arranged all things by measure and number and weight." (ch.11:20.) Nature is mathematically structured; it is ordered in this particular rational way. A German scholar has asserted that this was the most quoted biblical verse in the Middle Ages. And its source takes us right back into the end of the first millennium BCE when persecuted Jews in disorderly times were finding courage in God's provision of an orderly universe.

Church Declarations and a Duality Cosmology

Besides the speculations and arguments of individual scholars we may ask whether there were any official church pronouncements on these matters. Two of these were highly significant, especially in view of the increasing entrenchment of Aristotelian ideas and their great synthesis in the theology of Thomas Aquinas in the 13th century. The first is the decree of the brilliant Fourth Lateran Council of the whole church in Rome in 1214, a century before Buridan. This included rejection of any Greek ideas of the universe being eternal. It was created *ex nihilo* and in time, and so its contingent and de-sacralized nature was reaffirmed.

The second instance was initiated by the Pope and issued in the form of 219 propositions related to Aristotelian science that were condemned by the Bishop of Paris in 1277, primarily as guidelines for the University of Paris. It seems that certain of these were also taken up and applied to England by the Archbishop of Canterbury. The propositions included most of the matters we have been dealing with in the Hebraic cosmology and the Christian thinkers of the previous 12 centuries.

The list included the following: rejection of the eternity of the world and of the cyclic recurrence of its life every 36,000 years; the natural world was uniform in its constitution and laws, and stood in a contingent relation to its Creator; acceptance of the possibility of the void rejected by Aristotle; rejection of the heavenly bodies being animated and incorruptible, and of the influence of the stars upon human lives; and acceptance of the possibility of linear motion for the heavenly bodies, instead of the required circular movement obligatory in Greek science. All this was included in the intellectual inheritance of John Buridan in the same university in the next generation. Pierre Duhem went so far as to say that "modern science was born" on the day these decrees were promulgated; yet how many modern physicists and astronomers have ever heard of them?

Eliminating False Stereotypes

However that may be, these declarations did become everyday beliefs in the scientific world; but it was the church that was identifying and affirming them, as essential in the Christian cosmology that we have traced from its Hebraic origins. In popular parodies of the Middle Ages we hear about theologians being concerned with issues such as how many angels can stand on the point of a pin. On the contrary, here we have substantial secular issues being worked out, issues that had to be settled before science could emerge, and being worked on within ecclesiastical quarters where most of the best minds were available. A.N. Whitehead was right in drawing attention to what was going on in the Middle Ages in preparation for the scientific revolution to come.

The very fact that these declarations, in such detail, were necessary shows the range of issues still being discussed. I am aware that the two or three specific examples I have presented give little indication of the intellectual ferment of the Middle Ages, and of such contrary currents as neo-Platonism versus Aristotelianism, and of Aristotelianism itself. It was all so much more complex than we can handle here, by selection of only two of the main themes.

For instance, Aristotle died hard, despite the developments we have outlined, and no doubt assisted by the place of Aristotelian ideas in the great theological synthesis of Thomas Aquinas; indeed, some of the 219 condemned propositions were found in Thomas' own writings, although these were removed from the condemned list when he was canonized in 1323. As late as 1624 the Parliament of Paris threatened with the death penalty anyone who maintained doctrines differing from Aristotle.

Even in modern times there are persistent immanentist cosmological views that confuse God and the creation, and so return in principle to the encapsulated, unitive cosmology of the tribal cultures. This is found in Whitehead himself and his follower in developing 'process theology', Charles Hartshorne. These scholars would be horrified to have it pointed out that in these matters they were akin to their contemporary, National Socialism in Germany; here once again the tribal Aryan ground was holy, and the leader was the sacralized, god-sent *Führer*. This return to the primitive will engage us further below, and indicates that 'the battle of the cosmologies' is never finally concluded.[6]

But these comments are sufficient to dispel the stereotype of a dark and stagnant, anti-scientific period in European history from which the Renaissance and then the birth of modern science delivered us. There was in fact much more continuity between what went before and the scientific revolution that followed, than our artificial and in this case ignorant cutting up of history into periods allows for. Copernicus, Galileo, Descartes and the other 16th century pioneers of modern science knew and drew upon most of the figures we can name in the so-called Middle Ages; and indeed even further back, for we have seen that Galileo knew the key work of Philoponus, from a thousand years earlier.

All this might suggest that Aristotle and the Greeks could have avoided the nonsensical aspects of their theories if they had engaged in a little ordinary observation. What it really illustrates is the power of a thought-system, a cosmology, to control what one sees and how one interprets it. People like Plato and Aristotle were not stupid. Rather were they operating within a vast schema, an impressive and comprehensive cosmology that provided a framework for all their thought; observations were either rendered unnecessary (as with his wives' teeth!) or else were fitted in to this. Their problems lay not in their blindness to what may seem obvious to us, but in the very strengths of their cosmological framework, and how it controlled what they saw.

On the other hand, Buridan and many others were operating from a Christian view of a Creator and his contingent and de-sacralized creation that provided very different viewpoints and ways of understanding the data. Which cosmology one holds, dualist or duality (and once again the unitive also), becomes the determining factor. Scientific revolutions do not usually occur from the overwhelming weight of new factual, empirical evidence demanding a radically new theory. They come with new paradigms, new comprehensive visions, new worldviews, new cosmologies. Therefore we have been tracing something of the struggle between the dualist and duality views over one and a half millennia.

CHAPTER EIGHT

The Persistence of Dualism

AXIAL FAITHS AND THEIR DUALISMS

We must take a brief look, sideways as it at were, the other great Axial Age developments since the middle of the first millennium BCE. As A.N. Whitehead pointed out above, their incidental contributions to science or to technology cannot be compared with those of the Greek philosophers, much less with those of the early Christian Fathers, or even of the Arabs. Their pervasive dualism and lack of a proper form of contingency between the divine and the human ruled out a truly scientific development. And almost inconsistently with their dualist depreciation of the world, they continued to sacralize it: speculating on the eternal cycles of time, holding to their sacred relics and sacred places, and making their pilgrimages to the sanctuaries, building their holy temples and giving their social systems a sacred sanction. Their reforms of the encapsulated cosmologies were far from comprehensive.

Dualist Gnosticism and the Early Creeds

I have already referred to the anti-dualist theological evidence in the Christian thinkers of the early centuries, and in such creeds as that of Chalcedon. Theology was largely concerned in the early Christian period with a life and death struggle with powerful dualist religious systems, many of which came from the east and had ultimate links with some of the Axial faiths. We have mentioned the religion of Mani, Manichaeanism, from which Augustine made his belated escape.

This was one form of a whole complex of religions and philosophies gathered under the term Gnosticism, which included some, like the heretic Marcion, who regarded themselves as the true Christians. Here I can do no more than define these as various degrees of Gnostic dualism where escape from this unreal or temporary or distorted world into the eternal realm of pure spirituality was offered through special knowledge that was sometimes confined to the élites.

Against the Gnostics the early creeds were working out the implications of the incarnation of the authentic divine in the really human, in the person of Jesus. I have looked at the way a duality cosmology, in the doctrine of creation, was involved, and how separation between the two realms was rejected.

It was this very fact that lay at the heart of the theological problem with which the creeds were wrestling. William Temple, one of the great Arch-bishops of Canterbury in the 20th century, described Christianity, not in terms of its spirituality, but as 'the most materialist of all religions'. Our historical analysis would indicate that he was right.[1]

Dualist Christianity?

Instead of dealing with the detailed history of science since the mediaeval period, I shall deal further with the continuing description of Christianity as a dualist religion. I shall do this instead of pursuing the continuing dualism within the philosophy of science itself that runs from Descartes through Immanuel Kant and the neo-Kantians into recent times. The Cartesian tradition (i.e. from Descartes on, and not excluding the great Isaac Newton) has been well critiqued in the 20th century, especially by philosophers of science like Michael Polanyi and many others.

This matches the revolution in physics embodied in relativity and quantum theory. I shall take these methodological and philosophic critiques for granted, as not an essential part of the story we are tracing which appears at a more popular level and in many manifestations within our postmodern culture.

Despite the advances in articulating the biblical duality cosmology necessary for science, dualist interpretations of this faith persist, along with the accompanying classification, conscious or unconscious, of Hebrew religion among the Axial religions. Unless these can be disposed of, further exploration of the relations between science and Christianity becomes seriously distorted.

In Defence of Dualism

As a prime example of this dualism/Axial interpretation we have the various works of Professor Lloyd Geering, which have been influential in New Zealand and beyond. I have already used helpful quotations from his works in illustration of the Hebraic de-sacralization of nature, and of the world of the tribal cultures. Let me quote again on this point: "The natural world was becoming wholly de-sacralised; the natural forces were denuded of sacred power and humans had no need to fear them any more." So far, so very good.

But he then turns to the new seat of sacred power, which he repeatedly describes as "withdrawn from nature and seated in a supernatural world above." The corollary of this was the devaluation of this world. With this scenario he concludes with the remarkable statement that: "In none of the great religions was the dualism more pronounced than in Christianity."[2]

He then grants that this dualist view served two purposes in the past. It provided a standpoint from which to "to treat this world objectively as something humans could manipulate for their own ends."[3] There is a bit of a barb in these words, and they link up with those who blame our ecological problems upon an alleged Judaeo-Christian exploitation of nature. This describes some of the actual behaviour of the European peoples (but not these only), even while it inverts the biblical position of human responsibility for the development of creation to the glory of God.

The other purpose he recognises is to provide meaning from the other world for this world, for its origin and destiny and for our place in it. This is then declared to be a weakness, because it devalued this world as "a fallen world destined for final destruction."[4] This argument fails both in logic and in fact. There is no logical weakness in regarding this world as not self-contained and self-explanatory, and consequently finding its meaning in a higher realm; just the reverse – it guarantees the position of this world. And there is no factual accuracy here, for the orthodox Christian declaration has always been that a new heaven *and a new earth* will replace the present disrupted world. It has been a message of redemption and fulfilment, not of rejection and doom.

Wrong Classification

What has happened here is that the dimension of the divine in encapsulated cosmologies has been relocated in the upper realm of a dualist cosmology, as most of the Axial Age faiths and the major Greek philosophers did. It is then taken for granted that Christianity also belongs in this Axial Age and dualist category. Indeed there are those who want all religion referred to this other world – it is one way of keeping it out of an uncomfortable presence in politics or business!

This is certainly not Professor Geering's motive, but he has no other cosmology in which to place it. I have shown that this ignores the remarkable distinctives of the Judaeo-Christian tradition, and that these require a third cosmology. This I have called a duality, where the divine is radically distinguished from the created world, but never separated from it. Remember the Chalcedonian guidelines. Recognition of this third duality model disposes of the charge of dualism.

Return to the Tribal Model

But in fairness to those who adopt the dualist model, the historical outworking of the biblical duality model is not quite so simple. The tribal world, as we have emphasized, was integrated, or non-dualist, especially in the continuing relation of this world to the unseen one after death. This seems to have extended as far back as we can trace, for prehistoric burials show a very practical provision for the material needs of the dead in the after-life. And this after-life itself, with its Valhallas and its happy hunting grounds, was often an idealized version of life in this world,

In later cultural developments there seems to have been a desire to revert to this cosy system, despite the critiques that led to the Axial developments – to return to the cultural womb and to the apparent simplicities and wholeness of the primitive, which we shall examine in its contemporary forms below.

While the Axial Age religions depreciated the lower earthly realm, they were also busy re-sacralizing it with their relics, their sacred places and sanctuaries, and providing religious sanctions for their social systems, as I have already noted. They were ambiguous even about their own advances beyond the primal faiths.

The Appeal of the Dualist Model

This process is also conspicuous in Christian history, and not least, as we shall see, in our own day. There have been many examples of the depreciating dualist attitude, and I shall merely indicate some of them, together with their correctives in orthodoxy.

The first example might be those early Christians who despaired of this world and waited for the end of the age and the return of Christ. There have been many similar groups since, and there will be many more. But it is not as negative as it seems at first sight. These groups still use The Lord's Prayer with its plea for God's will to "be done, in heaven as *on earth*". They still look with intense faith for the new heavens and *the new earth*. They still read, probably very literally, the Genesis account of humanity's creation from both the *dust of the earth* and the spirit of God, and whether they do or do not use the Apostles' Creed they look for *the resurrection of the body,* as well as of the spirit or the soul, much as did those in the earliest cultures. Even these somewhat extremist groups look for the redemption of *this world*, and so contradict rather than illustrate the dualist thesis.

Other extremists occur in the early hermits who resemble the Indian holy men in their endeavour to escape from this world. These probably do serve this thesis, together with the admiration they aroused. But they were always exceptions, never typical, and I have already noted the much larger phenomenon of the monastic orders for their contributions to the development of the secular world.

These lay not only in the field of technology already mentioned, but also in guesthouses, hospitals, schools, and other forms of social service. Yet here again, the dualist motif edges back when manual labour in the monasteries is left to the lay brothers, while the choir monks engage in the really spiritual exercises, or impose harsh flagellations and other disciplines upon the body.

Then again, there are the enclosed orders, especially of nuns, who shut themselves off entirely from the world – but for what? – not to forget it, but the better to pray for its redemption!

The Opposing Christendom Model

Quite different evidence against dualism and on a large scale occurs in the great attempt to bring Christian control and order into the whole worldly life of a culture, that operated for the first half of the second millennium CE that we call 'Christendom'. When it collapsed in its unitary European form it continued in the 'little Christendoms' of national Christian states with their established Christianity, or the city-states like Calvin's Geneva.

The distinguishing marks of the latter include an affirmation of the secular structures and occupations of life as Christian 'callings' – the butcher, baker and candlestick maker – and so has contributed to the Protestant work ethic, together with a creation theology that strongly repudiates a sacred-secular dualism. True, in this period there was certainly much popular other-worldly piety, but it is a great mistake to take this as definitive, instead of the major thinkers and official forms that we have seen fighting dualist worldviews, and whose influence governed the future. In fact, some would criticize this period as being too worldly.

The Reaction from 'Worldliness'

Being too much of this world has always been a Christian refrain. It derives, however, not from depreciation of the world but in criticism of those who neglect the other world with its redeemed universe. These are called 'worldly' – a term that is easily misunderstood. Groups in legitimate reaction against this one-sided worldliness are also supported by the Christian view that this world shares in the fallen state of the human race, and so cannot be accepted simply as it stands. It also shares in the announcement of a total redemption for both the human race and for the world in which it lives.

Some of this does give support to the dualism thesis, but once it is looked into, much of it contradicts the dualist assessment. There will always be Christian groups that get it wrong, at least in the short run – groups that refuse to vote, to take part in community life, to use current technology, or to enjoy current forms of leisure and entertainment. The most astonishing example I know of in New Zealand is the small secession from the Maori Ratana Church, that unbelievably banned Maori, of all people, from particip-ation in rugby football!

Christian idealism has always reacted against a corrupt world with a certain 'other-worldliness'. Yet the Church has always explicitly defined itself over against such extreme views, while at the same time giving a certain honour to those who adopt these forms of spirituality. This recognises that there is always a little more going for these critical attitudes than there might seem to be. They do not, however, add up to presenting Christianity as a dualist religion.[5]

Renewed Concern for the World

But it is noteworthy how this dualist distortion of Christianity has been changing in my lifetime. I once would have written off the Christian Brethren assemblies in this way; now some of these have a remarkable record of social concern and service. The Evangelical Fellowship of New Zealand represents the wide range of conservative Christians, many of whom would regard the ecumenical Conference of Churches as too worldly. Yet in the 1990s the EFNZ called a meeting of the various evangelical agencies and societies whose agenda lies in the public sphere, and not with evangelism. There were no fewer than 22, and mostly formed since about 1990.

The so-called main-line churches were first linked together in the then National Council of Churches in New Zealand in 1941. This Council immediately mounted the largest combined Christian action ever to occur in this country, its Campaign for Christian Order in all dimensions of our national life. Despite its significance, it remains almost unknown today. It produced a remarkable series of booklets by highly competent authors on subjects such as work and wealth, sex, marriage and the family, and education; the author of one on the land later became Sir Alan Low, governor of the Reserve Bank. And Christianity is supposed to be a dualist, other-worldly religion! One now sees that this Campaign for Christian Order was too much in the Christendom mode, and this is one reason why it fell into oblivion along with that model.

I have given this attention to the dualist interpretation to show clearly that there is nothing here to interfere with the positive relation I have been tracing between the Judaeo-Christian tradition and the rise of modern science – in fact the commitment to a de-sacralized, contingent but fascinating universe ready for scientific study becomes even clearer.

CHAPTER NINE

Unexpected Confirmation
from Tribal Cultures

Mankind's Common Religious Heritage

Now I intend to turn to a highly relevant but unexpected and almost unknown confirmation of my thesis, to be found in the history of the relations between the tribal cultures and both the Axial and the Christian religions. The primal religions have already been described as forming 'humanity's common religious heritage', and the Axial and Abrahamic religions as forms of critique of this common background. All these later religions won their adherents from the tribal peoples of a large area, and after their consolidation remained in contact around their borders with the unconverted tribal societies.

But there it stopped and for over two millennia no substantial inroads occurred into the tribal faiths. The Greek tribes produced the great philosophic-religious systems of their culture but these did not produce viable public religious systems, either for the Greeks or abroad. Hinduism never won all the tribes even of the Indian sub-continent, for the forested peoples of northwest central India and those of the northwest forests and hill country remained apart from Sanskrit culture and its religion. Its main further location is in the Indonesian island of Bali, for special historical reasons.

Buddhism reached Tibet, China, Japan and the coastal peoples of southeast Asia, but never penetrated the hill tribes of the latter area. and settled down at the limits indicated. The Chinese faiths left the tribal peoples of the far west and the south untouched. Zoroastrianism became the faith of an empire spanning many peoples for a millennium but then withdrew to very narrow ethnic limits. And all the Axial faiths remained within the Asian continent, except for small diaspora and until very recent times. Their initial expansions within the tribal societies was not continued among the unconverted peoples still on their borders for the next two millennia.

Hebrew Tribes and a Duality Cosmology

The great exception to this impasse has been in one of the smallest of these tribal peoples (with its 12 named sub-tribes) who converted as a whole community to the new faith that we now call Hebrew or biblical, the religion of Israel. These developed the new duality cosmology that provided both a critique of tribal cosmologies and the alternative to the Axial dualisms, as well the cosmology for the Abrahamic religions that grew out of the Hebrew matrix, Judaism, Christianity and Islam.

Judaism has remained largely an ethnic non-missionary religion, making its unique contribution largely through its later offspring. Islam, the younger offspring, has expanded across many tribal peoples and won their allegiance, but has remained substantially within a broad band from Morocco to China, apart from the very recent immigrant communities in Europe and America. Its area of expansion has also brought it into contact with a wider range of tribal societies than any of the Axial faiths of Asia, and especially in Africa.

Tribal Peoples and the Christian Contact

I now turn to the interaction of tribal cultures and their religions with the immensely more powerful culture of the West and its accompanying Christian religion. Like the Axial faiths, Christianity made its initial expansion into the tribes on the borders of the area of its origin – those of Europe, western Asia and north Africa, and then settled down to consolidate and develop its Christendoms within these limits, and by and large ceased to be a missionary religion.

This limitation ceased with the great expansion of the European peoples into the rest of the world after Columbus. Fresh interactions commenced with the tribal societies in all other continents and new missionary opportunities and responsibilities emerged. About a generation after the first missionary contacts a new phenomenon appeared – the new religious movements that have appeared in large numbers in all continents, both on the borders of missionary areas and in their midst. These are indigenous developments, mostly at least intending to be Christian, however garbled their version of Christianity may be, but arising through their own founders in independence of local Christian missions, and usually in opposition to them. They are best seen as interaction movements between the two cultures in new contact and their religions.[1]

They have continued to appear in all the new continents since the 16th century and now include the cargo cults of Melanesia, other cults in the Pacific and especially the vast range in the Philippines, those in tribal India, the Peyote and other new religions among Native North and South American indigenous peoples, and thousands claiming to be independent churches in Black Africa and embracing many millions of members – that was where my own introduction occurred in 1957. In New Zealand the largest examples are the Ratana and Ringatu faiths, but no less than some 60 Maori interaction movements, however local or short-lived, have been traced since about 1820.[2]

Significant Features of Interaction Movements

I must confine myself to two of their most significant features. Firstly, they provide an excellent test case of what tribal peoples do when given access to the Christian religion but left to themselves to shape their response, without missionaries to protect, guide and control. They are indigenous developments, mostly at least intending to be Christian, sparked by the Christian contact even if quite slender, but in independence of local Christian missions, and usually in opposition to them.

The second feature is that this response shows various dissatisfactions with the tribal culture and religion, akin to those we saw giving rise to the Axial faiths. This is a kind of delayed replay of history. So the key question for our thesis on the cosmologies is which of the two alternative cosmologies do they move towards?

As I have pointed out, movements seldom emerge in the interaction with Hindu, Buddhist, Chinese cultures, and then move into their own independent forms of these Axial faiths – not even when they have the long contact and opportunity. The vast majority start to move from their original unitive, encapsulated cosmology into some form of a duality view derived from their own use of the Bible and from other Christian sources. The only other non-Axial faith to generate such interaction movements has been Islam, and its duality cosmology indirectly supports our thesis.[3]

Modernization: Choice of the Duality Model
The choice of the duality model, once it became available through Christian missions, coheres with frequent specific attempts at modernizing, at joining the developed world with its science and technology. This is where they see their future as new religious communities.[4] They are retaining their traditional wholeness, their union of the sacred and the secular, but in the new open, duality mode which de-sacralizes this world without separating it from the divine world.

This de-sacralization can be traced in the four key dimensions we identified in earlier Hebrew history, although this will of course be at various stages and forms in different communities.

De-sacralizing the Physical World
The first relates to the material world, which has previously been permeated by spiritual powers and controlled by magic and ritual that comes close to magic. The new movements characteristically repudiate magic, burn their fetishes, abandon their wasteful sacrificial rituals, and sometimes reject all traditional healing methods associated with diviners. They now rely on faith, prayer, fasting, communal support, and holy water. The latter of course may become a new magic, and the abandoned herbal remedies may include some losses. A New Zealand example of all this occurs at Ratana village near Marton; it has a meeting-house-style museum of discarded healing objects and practices. All this represents a massive cultural revolution in two basic senses. Magic is replaced by knowledge and science, and efficacious or manipulative ritual gives way to prayer and faith.

The second de-sacralization is interwoven with the first. It applies to sacred places, shrines and buildings. The places under taboo where the spirits dwelt are no longer feared and unusable. The old sanctuaries are destroyed or neglected, and replaced by new style churches for congregational assembly. Again there is the example of the great Kimbanguist church in Kinshasa in the Democratic Republic of the Congo (formerly Zaire), and the central church at Ratana Pa, and even if this is called their 'temple', it is essentially a meeting house for the community. The Maori didn't build temples or sanctuaries, and to this extent they were already closer to the new model.

De-sacralizing Time: From Myth to History

The third de-sacralization concerns time. Here the transition is from the mythical mode, with its primeval paradises and its culture heroes, into the historical mode. This has its known founders, its key historical dates, the new anniversaries celebrating these, and the great hopes for future expansion and influence. This also is a replay of the history of the Hebrew tribal people in relation to their own mythical past, and the transformation of their ancient festivals. Again, we have the example of the Ratana Church with its great annual January gathering, celebrating the birthday of its founder Wiremu Ratana, and the massive Easter assemblies of Zion Christian Church in the northern Transvaal.

This is a cultural revolution in the view of time, from myth to history. Its radical nature appears when we see that it often involves replacement of the biological tribal ancestors by a new spiritual genealogy anchored in the founder. He or she (for one of the new features is the number of women founders) may not even be of the same tribe as many of the members, but the founder's stories usually lead back into contact with Christian missions or their own use of the Bible.

In this way these new movements see themselves as a kind of new Israel, descended spiritually from the biblical peoples. Thus the remarkable Daku community of prophet Ratu Emosi away up the Rewa River delta in Fiji has its three satellite villages named Galilee, Antioch and Damascus. Some of these movements actually call themselves the Israelites as in South Africa, or in Uganda, the Bayudaya, the People of Judah. Some of the early Maori prophet movements also called themselves the *Hurai*, the Jews. And I wonder what might happen to the traditional biological *whakapapa* among the Ratana people, if they pursue their spiritual ancestry through Wiremu Ratana to the Methodists and Anglicans who were his Christian ancestors, and on back through the centuries to the biblical peoples, and to the ultimate common ancestors, Adam and Eve. These are the new identities available in such movements, and their new linkages to the human race.

This means that tribal peoples who were marginalized like the Africans in relation to the major developments of civilizations, or even lost to sight round the edges of the world, like the Maori – these peoples are now rejoining the human race through their own new religious movements. By de-sacralizing time they are re-entering world history, both in its past dimension and in its future course. Ratu Emosi in the Fijian community had amazing intricate charts of world and biblical history, leading up to his own Daku movement, now all part of the one story.

De-sacralizing Society

The fourth form of de-sacralization affects society, its structures and their religious sanctions. Some of these new movements remain essentially tribal, like the great Zulu church of Isaiah Shembe in Natal (note the biblical name revealing his own family Christian ancestry). Similarly, Ringatu in New Zealand has remained primarily Tuhoe people. But many others, like Ratana itself, achieve a transition to a trans-tribal membership, like the great Kimbanguist Church in the Congo that has spread into a dozen African countries and followed its members to Europe. Spiritual status has been transferred from the sanctified tribal system to the new tribe of the new God. Tribal religions have been dis-established and reduced to an option.

Further revolutionary features appear in that numbers of these movements are founded by young women – de-sacralizing, as it were, the traditional status of both age and gender. Equally striking, these new movements are voluntary religious societies. One chooses membership by some kind of conversion; one is not born into the only option. This also means that some people choose one among the many other movements that often arise in the same area. Both religious freedom, voluntarism and pluralism are dramatic changes essential for a democratic, open society in the modern world.

De-sacralizing Politics

These dis-established, voluntary religious societies also offer a new and most important source for critique of the political powers that is essential in a democracy. The leader of a West African independent church told me how in the 1950s he had been on an official visit to the President of the Republic of Liberia, President Tubman, a dictator who was a Churchillian figure perpetually associated with his cigar. When my friend was about to pray for Tubman, he first said: "Mr President; the Lord has something to say to you; will you put that cigar down?" No one dared speak to Tubman like that! And he put the cigar down. De-sacralizing the dictator, indeed!

The special significance of these movements is belatedly becoming recognized in South Africa. The largest such movement there is the Zion Christian Church. Each Easter many beyond their membership – up to several million people – travel from all over southern Africa for a great festival at their headquarters, Zion City Moriah.

For many years this festival has been ignored by others, but three weeks before the critical national elections in 1994, five leaders of the conflicting groups thought it worth their while to go away up to the far northern Transvaal to attend the Easter service together – President de Klerk himself, Nelson Mandela, Chief Buthelezi of the Zulu (Mandela's main political foe), the president of the Pan African Congress, and the leader of the Democratic party, one of the Afrikaner parties. Three weeks later there was the amazing story of the successful elections, even Chief Buthelezi having withdrawn his ban.

There were other Christian forces at work on the inside in these three weeks, but this independent African church was also a factor in critiquing the bitter political situation, and contributing to a peaceful democratic outcome. This is another example of the changeover effected by these movements from the single, sanctified tribal society to the plural, de-sacralized, modern, political community.

An Uncertain Struggle Across the New Nations

Whereas in Europe this de-sacralization struggle had to challenge the 'divine right of kings' and the Christendom attempts at a sacral culture, equivalent struggles are going on today in nations emerging from the tribal stage, as in Black Africa and in the southwest Pacific, and apart from these new religious movements. Traditional cosmology was of the encapsulated type, with closed religiously-sanctioned societies and sacral chiefs. The colonial powers brought 'open' Westminster-style two-party government, and at independence in the 1950s and 60s most new nations adopted this system in their constitutions. Then by the 1970s most had reverted to traditional, closed, one-party authoritarian states, often with dictatorial leaders, as in their past.

After a generation, this proved to be quite unsuitable for development and for participation in the modern world. So in the 1990s they began returning to perhaps more indigenous forms of the multi-party, more open, democratic system. This is a major cultural revolution, accompanied by much struggle and fresh forms of reversion, as when in the 1990s President Chiluba of Zambia, the newly-Christian President, declared his country to be a Christian nation, a reversion to an African Christendom that implied an encapsulated cosmology. Many of his enthusiastic European Christian supporters were embarrassingly naive as to what was really going on.

A different stage has been seen in the Christian nation of Tonga; here the 'Tonga-dom' of the ancient tribal faith was replaced by a Tongan Christendom in a Methodist form, and retained something akin to the divine right of kings. It is no accident that one of the leaders in the struggle for a more open and democratic system was a Catholic bishop whose own European culture and even his own church, have so recently been through the same de-sacralizing struggle.

Other nations have attempted reversions to the tribal faiths, as with the policy of 'cultural' (and hence religious) pre-Christian 'authenticity' in Zaire under Mobuto, or the government revival of tribal religion in Chad. These political manipulations of religions both soon failed. The comprehensive implications of return to the encapsulated cosmology were hostile to their entry to the modern scientific age. These are not remote political events peculiar to Africa, but rather indicators of how wide-ranging and all-embracing is the struggle between ancient encapsulated and modern duality cosmologies.

TRIBAL AND JUDAEO-CHRISTIAN COSMOLOGY AFFINITY

At this point I could pause to reflect on the special affinity between tribal cultures and the Judaeo-Christian tradition, shown not only in these new interaction religious movements but in the massive response of the tribal peoples since the Christian faith first spread into the tribal worlds of North Africa and Europe.

Since then there have been two further massive expansions of Christianity, into the tribal worlds of Black Africa and of Oceania, which can now be described as predominantly Christian culture-geographical areas. There have been no extensive expansions into the areas of the great Asian faiths founded in the Axial period or into Islamic areas, which maintain their identity despite highly significant and sometimes influential Christian minorities having grown up in their midst.

Deep-Rooted Affinity With the Duality Model

This most striking fact has not been examined by historians, but it carries a suggestion similar to that of the new movements from tribal cultures – that there may be some deep-rooted affinity between tribal or primal religions and the Judaeo-Christian tradition. They can recognise each other in a way that Buddhism, say, and Christianity cannot, and it suggests a counterpoint to the Asian Axials' resistance to Christianity.

This helps to explain the massive response of the Maori and other similar tribal peoples to the early missionaries – a response at their points of strength, in their leadership, rather than of weakness in their marginalised segments of society. So often, when Christian missions have engaged with tribal peoples, these have said: "This is what we have been waiting for." What has now been brought has fulfilled those searchings beyond the encapsulated world that we earlier noted in the prayers and hymns of the Inca, the Mbuti pygmies, and others.

This affinity lies in the Hebraic duality cosmology providing a more satisfactory critique of the encapsulated position than any of the Axial religions could offer. A duality cosmology distinguishes between the sacred and the secular but preserves a positive relation between them. This maintains the tribal peoples' sense of wholeness, by presenting a new and richer version of unity. Dualist cosmologies separate these two realms and depreciate the secular, the ordinary stuff of daily life. This offends the strong pragmatic emphasis in tribal cultures, with their closeness to the earth and to the things of this world.

Tribal Peoples Enter the World of Science

What might therefore have seemed like a digression into the subject of new tribal religious movements, and tribal responses to Christian missions, is rather a dramatic and unrecognised confirmation of our thesis as to the connections between a duality cosmology and the possibility of science. For tribal peoples the commonest route into the modern world of science and technology has been through missions that have brought to them the biblical

New Religious Movements Tribal

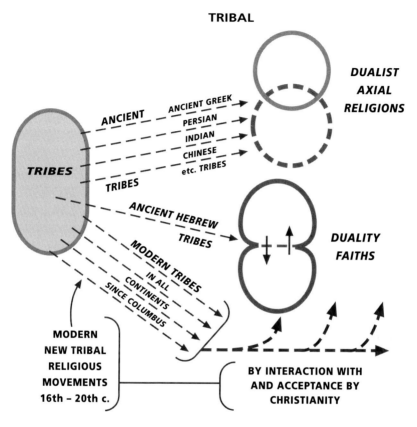

worldview, elementary education and medicine, including the beginnings of science, and some of the low-technology forms of development. Christian missions have been major agencies in the general de-sacralization of the tribal world that has begun. One cannot imagine this happening if the mission faith had been that of any of the great Asian or Axial religions. A Hindu or Confucian development of Papua New Guinea in a modern, scientific way with a university including science departments and a scientifically based medical school is quite inconceivable. The popular negative stereotype of Christian mission influence of course knows nothing of these matters and of the cultural levels at which they operate.

CHAPTER TEN

Reversionist Spirituality
in the 20th Century

There is no way of taking account of any of the above massive religious changes in tribal peoples in a schema that Professor Geering has presented, in terms of three stages in human culture: first the tribal, ethnic era, then the trans-ethnic religious era, and now the global, secular, this-worldly era of modern science.[1] These periods or stages correspond exactly with those of the 19th century Cambridge armchair anthropologist, Sir James Frazer, in his famous and popular book *The Golden Bough*.[2] He calls them simply the stages of magic, religion and science. They may be set out as follows, with my corresponding cosmology:

MAGIC, RELIGON AND SCIENCE
UNITIVE COSMOLOGIES Era of Magic: Tribal, ethnic cultures, followed by paradigm change to:
DUALIST COSMOLOGIES Era of (Axial) Religions: Trans-ethnic, universal, followed by paradigm change to:
↓
UNITIVE COSMOLOGIES Era of Science: Modern science, secular, post-religious. 'The New Age'.

The Return of the Sacred

The above schema was supported by the sociologists' thesis of inevitable secularization – that religion was moving to the margins of an increasingly secularized society and would survive as a personal affair for a diminishing minority. This thesis survived into the 1960s and still operates for some sociologists. The more the 20th century has proceeded, the more this has been proved wrong. Let me merely list some of the signs of the 'return of the sacred' in this unpredictable century.

1. There has been more religious innovation across all religions than in any previous century, as witness the many thousands of new tribal religious movements that have arisen, and the proliferation of the so-called 'sects and cults' in Western societies since the 1950s, together with the manifold and new charismatic movements within Christianity. These are public and corporate innovations, not the individual, private versions that were prophesied by some of the sociologists.

2. There have been major religious expansions: Asian faiths have moved into the wider world as both migratory and missionary, and Christianity has experienced its greatest growth ever, as in Black Africa, Oceania, and parts of Indonesia, India and Korea. Hence there have been more churches built in this century than in the whole of the rest of Christian history. Apart from missionary expansion, for 1990-93, the three largest religions in the world, Christianity, Islam and Hinduism, reportedly grew faster than the world population.

3. In a self-conscious and sophisticated fashion there have been revivals of faiths thought long dead, such as the earlier pagan tribal religions of Europe and the occult and Gnostic cults we have mentioned earlier – there are even public so-called educational courses in Western countries, not just studying these, but promoting their practice, and even creating religions that never existed, such as the the supposed early European Great Goddess cult, which we shall mention again later.

4. There has been more religious persecution, and more Christian martyrs, than in any previous century; and what is of no importance because it is socially marginal or on the way out (as social theory had it) does not get persecuted. This persecution receives publicity in the non-Western world, but if I were to stop and document in detail the unrecognised religious persecution in so-called tolerant Western countries such as New Zealand, Australia,

and the United States of America, you might be astonished and horrified.

5. Somewhat related to persecution is the extent to which the religious factor enters into and complicates violent political conflicts late in the 20th century, as in Ulster, the Balkans, parts of the former Soviet Union, Israel, the Sudan, Sri Lanka and the Philippines. In four of these seven areas, and in other conflicts since 1980, Islam is one of the parties involved, and there are those who predict that the world problem of Marxism in the 20th century will be replaced by that of aggressive and intransigent Islam in the 21st century.

By and large the religious dimension does not vanish; it reappears in new, strange, pervasive and creative or destructive forms; and when threatened, it reaffirms itself in the various fundamentalisms. The secularization of the world, and the new faith in secularism, have not been as inevitable and all-embracing as we were promised. And in formerly encapsulated societies where the secular has been distinguished from the sacred in a new duality cosmology, this has been a necessary advance for the move into science.

Back to the Womb: Reversions to the Encapsulated World

All these studies of religion, whether tribal, Axial, Judaeo-Christian or modern innovative movements, indicate that instead of the new age marking the transition, according to the scheme above, from the world's religions to faith in the new scientific age, the religious faiths are very much alive. Ironically, at the same time that modern science is under its first major threat since its birth in the 16th century; this attack takes two forms, one more oblique and the other more direct.

The Oblique Attack on Science

The oblique form is manifest in modern Western societies in the many signs of reversion to the tribal encapsulated world, and rejection of the Judaeo-Christian duality cosmology.

The view of God as the creator distinct from creation is at issue again in Western culture. Despite the emphasis on the 'Wholly Other' by Rudolf Otto and on the otherness of God by Karl Barth (probably the two most influential 20th century writers on religion), the later part of the century has seen a revival of the unitive, encapsulated view of the more primitive societies.

Religious Reversions

This revival is many-sided – it appears in the panentheism of process theology and in Matthew Fox's 'creation spirituality'; it runs deep in all the Hindu-related gurus and Asian mysticisms, the new occultisms and paganisms penetrating the West; many of the New Age movements and teachings declare that All is One, the divine, ourselves and nature; or God is *in* me as my potentiality and so I am divine. These movements represent a loss of nerve, a kind of throw-back by a culture in great distress, a rejection of the fundamental lessons and advances of at least three millennia, a reversion to the womb where all is safe and warm – to the encapsulated world. Again, I can but list some of the more specific signs:

1. The return of magic and the occult to fashion among the same educated Westerners who not long ago, as heirs of the Enlightenment, despised both magic and religion as 'primitive superstitions'. Sophisticated bookshops in major cities specialise entirely in these areas, and where scholarly works on religion were once to be found in the better bookshops, these are now over-shadowed by large sections on magic and the occult. Magic in this context has nothing to do with stage or party illusions but represents a worldview. One report from a participant/observation study made in 1990-93 in London is too illuminating not to quote:

> ...the aim of much magical practice is to develop the 'true'...self...to put the magician (the microcosm) in touch with the larger whole (the macrocosm)...a rebellion from what magicians perceive to be a dualistic culture...Christianity...is dualistic – is seen to externalize evil by opposing Satan to God in the battle between good and evil...magical ritual is seen to be a holistic healing space...where the magician can contact his/her inner world and the wider cosmos. The ideal aim of ritual practice is personal transformation which...can lead to a knowledge or 'gnosis' of the Divine.[3]

This illustrates perfectly so much of our position – the interpretation of Christianity as dualistic, the reversion to the 'holistist' or unitive cosmology where the microcosm matches the macrocosm, or the 'inner world' matches 'the wider cosmos'. This is the cosmology of the primal encapsulated world-view mixed up with the incompatible cosmology of Gnostic dualism. Logic and reason have flown, and an eclectic DIY religion has been invented for customer satisfaction. When feminist ideologies are added to subvert the ordinary meaning of 'witchcraft' in the same way that 'magic' has been subverted and even reversed in effect, then a different trajectory appears: the origins of the new witch-cults are then located in a golden matrifocal age where women and 'Nature' are revered before "urban cultures of conquest with their patriarchal religions divided spirit from matter, shattering...the former symbiotic wholeness."[4] This of course is an Orwellian ideological rewriting of history within the categories of this present study or by subversion of the language.

2. In this allegedly post-religious age we are witnessing the emergence of organised religious cults openly and proudly taking the name of paganisms or witchcraft and organising their own literature, associations and conferences. Some of this reversion proceeds to the development of Black Magic cults and Satanic religions, which mock Christian rituals by blasphemous inversions into Black Masses or by sexually perverted rituals. I once led a group of theological students that met weekly in the drug area of Atlanta in a room where the walls were besmeared with satanic signs written in human blood by the previous occupants, one of these cults. This of course is far from reversion to the authentic religions of tribal societies; it represents a modern mistaken recreation of what the primitive is thought to have been, as something the direct opposite of current Christian forms, despite our suggestion of an affinity between them. And it is motivated by a violent reaction from the Judaeo-Christian tradition in all its dimensions, including the scientific.

3. Somewhat more authentic is found in the overtones of the ecology movement which amount to a restored animism, a re-personification of nature, that speaks of our mother, the earth, and our brothers and sisters the plants and animals. This goes even further when nature is divinized and we are invited to worship the earth goddess in a re-sacralized world – an invitation issued by a New Zealand university, and no doubt elsewhere, as we shall see in a moment.

4. One specific form is the sacralization of the body, the cult of physical fitness, strength, sporting prowess, of the ideal male and the beautiful female, and all these entrenched in the entertainment world – this body-cult supports large industries from work-out gymnasia to cosmetics to plastic surgery. The

body has become the sacred object of a new religion that makes absolute demands and consumes resources away beyond the normal concerns with health and a decent appearance.

5. A specific aspect of this is the sacralization of sex in any of its forms. This is akin to the basic place of fertility rites in tribal cultures, and their continuation in the form of sexual partners for rites in the temples of both pre-Axial and Axial religions. This serious purpose has been changed in the modern forms, where communal fertility concerns have been replaced by individual psychological anxieties. Sex is now elevated to the position of determinant of the individual identity of a person (in my essence I am a hetero/homo/bi-sexual being), and as the clue to human fulfilment and happiness – 'seek ye first the full sex-life and all else will be added unto you'. In effect, both the body and sex have ceased to be gifts of God for our welfare and have themselves become as gods, controlling our lives as first priorities and ultimate reference points.

These developments have provided a whole new field of research in religious studies departments in Britain, and I am indebted to some of their preliminary results, which I shall draw on again a little later.[5]

Neo-pagan Motivations and Tribal Spirituality

These neo-paganisms are also motivated by a rejection of modern, secular and scientific society, and also of Christianity. Both are seen as opposite forms of dualism – secular society in being opposed to the sacred, and Christianity as being otherworldly and setting good against evil – hence the Satanic cults eliminating this difference.

The new paganisms seek a holistic world, and think to have found it in a highly idealised and unhistorical image of the 'noble savage' in a primeval 'Golden Age' free from the later decadence of the modern Western world. This is a direct return to the non-historical view of time, to the corruption of life over the course of time,[6] and to the need for renewal by return to the primeval past.

In Britain the noble savages were the ancient Celts, with their spiritual teachers the Druids, who are seen as the exemplars of a spirituality that has been lost and is now being revived. In North America the fashion is to take up with Native American religions; and in all areas the faiths of the indigenous peoples, as they are called, are experiencing attempted revivals.

These revivals, however, are not tied to historical facts, nor are they put to the test of providing a whole community with a viable, public, religious system – for that is what earlier tribal religions did. Instead, such revivals now lie at the mercy of ideological and political forces, as is clearly seen in much revived tribal 'spirituality'; this stands in contrast to the authentic religion found in the new community religious movements we have surveyed.

Tribal faiths are now reconstructed to suit the political demands of indigenous peoples (who themselves know little more of their real past than anyone else). When these demands are for land compensation, local 'spirituality' is enlisted in support by means of an idealised version of the relation of their ancestors to the land. This version re-sacralizes it and so removes it from the very form of scientific development that has since brought out its potential, and that offers it a still more fruitful future. To emphasize the inherent sacrality of the land is a self-defeating tactic in the end, and needs to be replaced by a different attitude of respect for and responsibility towards the earth that avoids re-sacralizing it.

Maori Re-spiritualizing in New Zealand

Equal vagueness marks the new correctness of invoking tribal 'spirituality' at every opportunity. We take current examples using Maori religion in New Zealand, where it is politically correct to open every new organization or building, specially connected or not with Maori, with a Maori 'blessing', or with *karakia*, allegedly traditional prayers in Maori.

This applied, though not without controversy, to the new Museum of New Zealand in Wellington. Even the new Tamaki campus of the University of Auckland received a dawn blessing ceremony. It thus kept company with the nearby new Courtyard Bar replacing an old hotel in the suburb of Glen Innes – in 1994 this was blessed by two Ratana Church ministers. The founder Ratana himself was so hostile to alcohol among Maori, and to traditional Maori religion in general, that he would surely have withdrawn the church credentials of ministers who tangled with these things.

But it is not only the Ratana Church, for in another Auckland suburb in the same year an Anglican bishop and a Methodist conference president were joined with other church leaders and the local Maori tribe in a dawn ceremony of blessing a new church site with fresh spring water. And then even the Maori art works, or *taonga*, were installed in the new Auckland casino with a dawn blessing. Strange company, this imported and so pakeha (i.e., European) institution, for the allegedly traditional Maori practice! Or is this indeed what multi-culturalism means – an indiscriminate conjunction of activities without authentic historical precedent or modern meaning?

Encapsulating Cosmologies Revived

The common choice of the dawn and the use of 'fresh spring water' indicate that the sacredness of these actions (if they are to have any such meaning) is tied to the rhythms of the cosmos and the resources of nature, and so to an encapsulated cosmology. The historical world of a biblical cosmology is a far remove from the nature-religion of this neo-paganism. Even senior church leaders, and Maori leaders, including some from one of the new religious movements I have described, along with the authorities of a modern university (with the statutory duty of being 'the critic and conscience of society'!), even all these are naively unaware of the reversion they are encouraging in these new DIY forms. The confusions of multi-culturalism have much to answer for.

As the British studies point out, these are not authentic revivals of tribal religions, and for several reasons. Firstly, they are not motivated primarily by religious concerns such as worship and salvation in a spirit of humility, or with a true and universal faith uniting all people. They are promoted by somewhat aggressive Maori groups concerned with their own political influence and the establishment of their human rights. These may be quite legitimate concerns, but the appeal to allegedly Maori spirituality has become another example of the familar manipulation of religion for other purposes.

Secondly, this is a highly sanitized Maori spirituality. The particular forms chosen have been screened through Western and Christian moral criteria to eliminate anything connected with such aspects of Maori warrior culture as warfare and its connected slavery and cannibalism, and its associated patriarchal and male-dominated features.

Thirdly, as already pointed out, these practices are only bits and pieces, abstracted from the original religious complex to which they belonged. In no sense do they represent the return to a viable, public, religious system for a whole community. Technically, in religious studies, these bits and pieces should properly be called superstitions – a kind of spiritual debris which the adherents of former religions attempt to revive or keep alive within the context of a new system which is really incompatible with them. This is a necessary concept in religious studies and in no sense the derogatory term it has become in popular usage; at the same time the deliberate perpetuation of superstitions is most undesirable.

The Alleged Great Goddess Cult

In New Zealand there are also attempted throwbacks to the earlier religions of pre-Christian Europe. One notorious example of this was the course in 1993 in the Centre for Continuing Education of the University of Auckland, entitled 'Speaking with the Ancient Goddess'. This occupied 12 hours over a weekend, and it promised that "We will view images of the Great Goddess in her various aspects and then interact with her through body movement, dance, ritual, drawing and writing...[and] we will discover more about the goddess power we hold within ourselves as women. No special experience or skill is necessary...Please bring...writing materials, a cushion and a candle..."

This clearly goes beyond the academic study of religion into actual promotion and practice in a public, allegedly secular institution, 'interacting' with the pagan Goddess and using ritual paraphernalia (the candle, etc.). Note that the course was gender-restricted to 20 women, thus making the practice more intensive or effective. If an equivalent Christian course were offered there would be a howl of protest. In fact there are properly academic courses on Christianity for the University's degrees in theology. By contrast these are open to all faiths and both genders, and there is no promise of interaction with the deity in the classroom!

Worse still for a university is the fact that this goddess cult in Europe never existed. It is a creation of the modern, extreme feminist movement. Let the great *Encyclopaedia Britannica* make its own confession on this subject (1995, vol.25, p.96). Its article on witchcraft tells the story when referring to the modern witchcraft or 'wicca' movements:

> These so-called witches claim to be adherents of an ancient religion, the one to which Christianity is regarded as a counter religion...These... sincere but misguided people...have been directly or indirectly influenced by Margaret Murray's article 'Witchcraft'...in the...*Encyclopaedia Britannica* (1929), which put forth...her theory that the witches of Western Europe

were the lingering adherents of a once general pagan religion...displaced...by Christianity.

After protests by historians, 'this highly imaginative but now discredited' article by a scholar with academic credentials corrupted by an ideology, was dropped from the *Britannica*!

But despite this information in the library, the same false historical thesis returned in the University of Auckland as a course on a pre-Christian, separate, women's cult of the Great Goddess, artificially constructed for ideological purposes, and promoted by a woman with a Ph.D. True, there were plenty of goddesses in early European religions, but there was no special women's cult of this nature. Someone in the Centre for Continuing Education ought to be reading the confession of error in the University's *Britannica*, or else abandoning their 'Mission Statement' of providing 'access to the distinctive educational expertise...the scholarship, research, skills and values of the wider University.' In this case it would have meant checking with the theological faculty.

All this in a modern university that claims to be recognized as among the world's élite group of 21 best institutions, and which operates under an education act requiring universities to be 'the critic and conscience of society'! Any protest or exposure of similar academically worthless, ideological courses year by year in the religion, philosophy or psychology offerings, would have rebounded on the protester.[7] It should be said that the University of Auckland is not alone in this nonsense, for similar examples could be found elsewhere in New Zealand, in Britain, and especially in the USA.

'Designer Religions' and their Attack on Science

Finally, and by way of summary, these are not authentic revivals of tribal faiths in their wholeness, and governed by factual and historical accuracy. They are what we might call, in the modern idiom, 'designer religions', artificially created for purposes ulterior to those of religion. In this sense they express the multi-cultural ideology which asserts that all cultures are relative, and so each community can have its own culture designed and constructed for its own conscious needs. There is therefore an underlying unity with the so-called constructivist, pupil-centred theory that has become official in New Zealand education and is still influential elsewehere. Religion, culture and science also, it seems, can all be constructed to suit ourselves. The Maori and similar indigenous tribal peoples are to be encouraged to develop 'Maori (or whatever) spirituality and science' and Europeans to work within 'Western religion and science'. To impose the latter on the Maori or other such peoples is cultural imperialism.

If these remarks seem too severe or exaggerated, let me quote from some of the British religious studies research reports. One of these speaks of new DIY cultural mixes; of cultural transvestism; of the collage approach selecting from many tribal religions and ignoring the differences that are important to their own adherents; of spiritual consumer shopping in the global religious supermarket, unrestrained by history, tradition or truth; of a spiritual imperialism that invades tribal religions, not to join them, but to plunder them in a new religious colonialism and imperialism! One can only agree with the sharp truth expressed in these vivid ways.[8]

Even with this support from scientific religious studies, my suggestion that all this is in effect a current religious attack on science will seem wildly exaggerated. But it will so appear only to those who have not recognized the return to an encapsulated re-sacralized world where there is no place for science. These developments are all the more dangerous in that their profound cultural significance is unrecognized, and that they do not and cannot at this stage of history, represent or revive authentic tribal religions. These, as we have shown, did have their own genuine dimensions of spirituality that are lacking in their would-be successors. The latter fall between all the cosmological stools, and there is no place for them in the Frazer/ Geering schema, to which I shall return in a moment.

CHAPTER ELEVEN

Religious and Scientific Reversions

Historians of religion are well aware of reversions in religions, which lie behind the need for repeated reformations – *semper reformanda,* as the Protestant Reformers put it. "The Axial traditions have always shown a tendency to revert to pre-Axial forms."[1] I have already referred to some of these, and I indicated that in Hebrew cultural history the de-sacralization of the four dimensions of matter, time, space and society was a long and uneven process. This reflects the fact the tension between the two cosmologies never vanishes, and the de-sacralization has to be continually fought for if science is to develop in the first place, and to survive later challenges.

This is evident, even when we consider only the dimensions of matter and space, when Jews call their synagogues 'temples' and add overtones of the temple to their synagogue buildings and interiors. Many ultra-orthodox Jews avoid this and pine for the full restoration of the Jerusalem Temple and its ritual system, animal sacrifices and all. Christians revert likewise in Gothic cathedrals with their numinous effects, to relics and pilgrimages to holy places, and to churches described as 'houses of God', laid out with internal sanctuaries. Even Muslim mosques attempt to 'make the building say it in its own right', and introduce echoes of the temple type. And of course the temples of the Axial religions have always been sacred buildings and places.

Rejections of Western Culture and Science

Developments within the postmodern movement in the last third of the 20th century represent not the struggle to escape further from the encapsulated world, but rather to return to it from a modern, Western cosmology allied with the duality model and its scientific expressions. This is a wholly new and surprising phenomenon, an escape from the Frazer/Geering model with its promise of a new scientific age. Geering actually gives a sympathetic account of the new nature mysticism of Teilhard de Chardin, of James Lovelock's *Age of Gaia, A Biography of the Living Earth*, and of some in the Greenpeace movement, and correctly identifies these as forms of reversion to the animist, pre-Axial stage. At the same time he rightly warns us that "this does not mean that we should simply venerate the earth in the way the ancients venerated the earth-mother Gaia. We are to value the earth, but not to worship it as an object from which we stand apart."[2]

This sees the danger of re-sacralization, and is well said. It fails, however, to come to terms with the 20th century explosions of religion, the massive 'return of the sacred', and with the extent, the variety, the pervasive nature and the novelty of the massive return to the primitive among the least likely, the educated and affluent classes of our own modern and largely scientific society. This unprecedented, irrational development goes away beyond the kind of reversions already noted in the dualist Axial religions. It has no place in the promises of the Frazer/Geering schema, and will not be checked by warnings such as I have just quoted. It demands a deeper analysis, in terms of the duality model that is being ignored.

Cultural Relativism Embraces Science

Besides these contemporary cultural reversions there are many other forces lined up in Western societies with radical criticisms of science. The postmodern era had arrived, at least among many intellectuals and in the media, and this meant the end of the modern scientific era which it was publicly assumed lay ahead of us. The belief in the existence and at least partial apprehension of one, common, international scientific truth, grounded in the nature of reality itself, has given way to the subjective beliefs or reactions of individuals or groups, of sub-cultures or whole cultures, which change with their situations and experiences.

This is cultural relativism, with the assumption that all cultures are equal in terms of meeting the needs of different societies, and with the corresponding battle-cry of multi-culturalism, when understood within this context. In the field of science this soon becomes scientific relativism or 'multi-science', with each people or culture doing their own science in their own terms – Maori, European, Indian 'science', 'physics', etc.

Without this particular intention, Thomas Kuhn's influential *The Structure of Scientific Revolutions* moved in this direction. For him there was no rational continuity between the classical physics of Newton and the relativity physics of Einstein, and no rational, scientific way of deciding for one view rather than the other – they 'practise their trades in different worlds'. The decision is made by our culture and society as over against Newton's society.[3]

Besides the cultural and therefore scientific relativists there are various other groups actively joining in the discrediting of science, and of its associate, technology. Some ecologists charge science with destructive exploitation of nature; the anti-nuclearists regard it as polluting and death-dealing; the peace movement sees it as militaristic; some in the women's movement as patriarchal and male-dominated; the socialists, as the tool of capitalism and multi-national corporations; the educational constructivists, as a dogmatic imposition upon the pupil. It is surprising that any scientist can still lift up his head. Analysis of these varied protests would reveal many a longing for reversion to the primitive and the encapsulated world, but there is much else at work here, a sheer disillusionment with 'Faith's New (Scientific) Age' itself, as adequate for the future.

Subversions Within Science Itself

There are still further problems in the new scientific scheme of things. These concern the widespread subversion of science, not only from within our modern culture generally, but from within the science community itself. Here I can but list some of the outward signs of these new and scary times in my own as a typical Western society, signs that seem minor in themselves but assume new significance when seen as indicators of a major reversion. We have already mentioned the then New Zealand Minister of Education's repudiation of concern to discover truth about reality in his scientific doctoral research. This consorts with his Ministry's adoption of a constructivist educational philosophy in the new national curricula for science and five other areas, despite the profound criticisms to which it has been subjected by some of the country's best minds. It also consorts with the sad remark made to me by a university vice-chancellor, himself a scientist, that the universities were no longer interested in truth.

This is evidenced in the growth of new courses in tertiary education on subjects of very uncertain scientific or academic status, such as those in various forms of alternative medicine,[4] of manifold psychotherapies, or of human development. Nursing schools have been invaded by disruptive ideologies, especially of New Age affinities, and by 'cultural sensitivity' courses that exalt Maori and similar spiritualities. Serious students have been driven to protest, and often paid a substantial cost for doing so.

I have heard it suggested (and by one of the top scientists in New Zealand) that one university science faculty had so abandoned the concern of pure science with truth for its own sake, and had so surrendered to the pragmatic demands of current society for problem-solving and technology, that it might well be disbanded. And others would say the same of the New Zealand Qualifications Authority. Its 1995 School Certificate paper in science contained flawed questions that could not be answered, set by examiners showing ignorance of basic scientific principles. The Institute of Physics protested, and candidates had their papers re-marked. But the first NZQA spokesman, instead of confessing, apologizing, and hastening to amend, actually defended the error as representing one among various points of view! So sense and nonsense were of equal status in our science education.

Other queries as to the state of science arise in more sophisticated issues. Among some scientists there is a flirtation with Eastern mysticisms and their associated dualist worldviews that would destroy science itself. Thus Stanley Jaki summarized physicist Fritjof Capra's view that "the Taoist outlook is taken for a prophetic anticipation of the 'true' message of quantum theory."[5] This influential but cosmologically naive scientist presents quantum theory as holding that the human observer and the observed object, and the ultimate constituents of objects themselves, do not exist as separate entities, but only in mutual interaction. Something of this is a mark of the new physics, but in this loose popularization it is then equated with Eastern mysticisms that stress the interconnectedness of all things, but wherein the worshipper is finally united with the divine and loses separate identity, so that there is neither science nor scientist. As we have earlier indicated, the first question then would be why Taoist China, with all its advanced civilization and varied technology, did not develop science, but has had to import it from the West.

The problem is properly attacked from the model of the Christian Trinity, where both unity and diversity are exemplified without either being abandoned to the other, and with help of the four Chalcedonian guidelines. Here our understanding of mutual interaction is preserved from solutions that fail to maintain the identity of the entities that are being related, that fail to see them as both inseparable and yet always distinct. In other words, the duality cosmology must be preserved for science, and these views teetering between dualist and encapsulated cosmologies must be resisted. And not only by scientists, but by theologians who hover round quantum theory, the ideas of chance and of the Big Bang in the wrong-headed hope of finding a basis for their theology in the more prestigious natural science. They already have the basis in the biblical duality cosmology they share with the scientists themselves.

SUMMARY OF OUR JOURNEY

As we move towards the final stages of this survey, let me look back upon where we have travelled:

1. We established the lineaments of the tribal, unitive, encapsulated cosmology, its strengths and its internal critiques and incompatibility with science.

2. We then outlined the dualist cosmologies of the great civilizations and the major new religions of the Axial Age, and of the Greek religious philosophies. Despite the appearance of the genuine scientific attitude and some tentative contributions among the Greeks, and great technical advances, especially in China, science did not appear.

3. Then we examined the Hebrew people, who also exhibited some of the advances found in the Axial faiths, but went beyond these by de-sacralizing matter, space, time and society and so developed a third model of cosmology we called a duality model. This excluded Hebrew religion and its Judaeo-Christian successor from the Axial group, and this distinction became the core of our thesis – that in this cosmology lay the essential prerequisites for the rise of science, although the Hebrews did not follow through and develop any science.

4. This thesis was then supported by an extended historical survey of the thinking about the world, and about basic issues in physics such as motion, among the best minds of the early Christian centuries, and then in the Middle

Ages. This thinking finally ousted the Aristotelian physics that had persisted, and then it proved to be in continuity with modern science when this appeared in the 16th century, for which the earlier work provided the essential if not the sufficient conditions.

5. A dualist view of Christianity was then found in error in the light of the Judaeo-Christian duality cosmology, of the history of Christian thought about this world, of the positive relation of Christian theology to science, and, unexpectedly, of the choice of the duality model by the new religious movements among tribal societies since the 16th century in their moves towards modernization.

6. These also testified to the contradiction of the secularization thesis on the decline of religion, and to the massive manifestations of religion in the 20th century. These include the religious reversions to the encapsulated cosmology, and the new 'designer religions', all of which threaten science.

7. Further threats to science occur from various quarters in Western postmodern, relativistic culture, including subversions from within science itself. The signs of this leading to the collapse of science and the replacement of all cosmology by nihilism will engage us until we reach the final chapter on the interdependence of science and religion.

Science and the Christian Religion – A Reversed Dualism?

It will now be apparent that history, both past and recent, rejects the whole Frazer/Geering schema within which many in Western societies have seen the relations between science and religion. Their future relations, therefore, are likely to be very different from these expectations. Let me first sketch the future as this schema presents it, in the terms of our cosmology models.

I think it would be agreed that science has no adequate roots in the two cosmologies, unitive tribal and Axial dualist; indeed, that it is incompatible with them. Then it seems that one might settle for an inverted form of the dualist model. By this I mean a radical reversal in the realities of the two worlds. This material world and our life in it would then be the only real and ultimate world, and science would be our major resource in handling it. The 'spiritual' other world of the dualist model would then lose its status of a superior and ultimate reality, and would be reduced to a Platonic shadow in reverse, a mere shadow of this world, or a mere spiritual reflection or appearance without substance.

This position then commonly reverts to the 19th century Feuerbach theory of religion as a psychological projection, and spells out the status of our religious beliefs in what is an application of the same constructivist theory found in education quarters. The difference is that what was applied to science and to all knowledge is now applied in reverse, as it were, to religion, rather than to science, which some would protect from this subversion. But we have seen how this is a difficult task in a society where everything is increasingly regarded as a cultural construct.

To save the religion thus constructed, however, an essential place is found for 'faith' in the New Age, even if we do have to manufacture it ourselves. It is asserted that we cannot live without some form of faith. Since it has no objective anchorage or fixed form or existence in a higher reality 'out there' or anywhere else, we are free to draw on any of the religious traditions, tribal or Axial, and especially on Christianity, for construction materials, for ideas and practices for the new faith, and to remodel these to make them suitable for use in our new, scientific, this-worldly context.

It seems clear that this position can be understood in terms of what we may call a reversed dualism model. This stands firmly within the Enlightenment tradition that we call 'modernity', whereby the real, objective world belongs to science and its study of facts, and religion and morality belong to the subjective realm of opinion about values, which remain important but depend upon our own constructions. This is why such views have had strong appeal to those who see themselves as belonging to the modern world.

Post-Modernism: The Collapse of all Cosmology

It is difficult for the scientific or the commonsense mind to take this seriously: a faith that in the end reduces to talking to one's self, and yet we must do so, and now more so. Since the 1960s the modernity stage of Western culture has been overtaken in overt ways by what we call 'postmodernity'. The chief further development here is extension of the relativity which the modern attitude applies to religion, to science itself.

We have noted above some of the signs of this total cultural relativity, which has now engulfed the world of science itself, and removed this last bastion of objectivity, with its concept of objective truth. All is now mere opinion, or the product of the various cultures rather than of the one, common reality. The Frazer/Geering position can no longer claim to lead to

Unstable Reversed Dualism

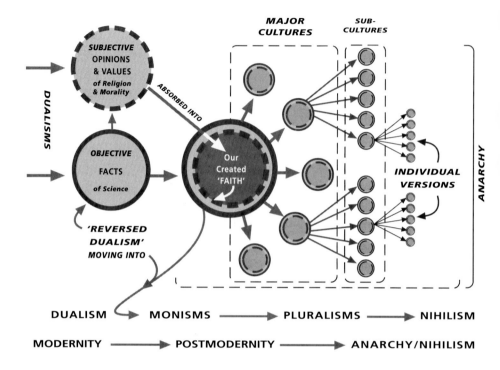

a climax in modern scientific thought; it has been left behind by further developments which undermine it.

There is a good deal to be said for those who see postmodernity as the further and inevitable development of the Enlightenment or modernity position, and therefore call it 'ultra-modernity'. My discussion then is really a critique of both main trends in contemporary Western culture, of modernity and postmodernity. This critique is made from the stance of the third model for cosmology that has been so influential in the earlier history of science, but has been ignored in our society, and even lost sight of in the churches where it ought to be nurtured.

Settling for this reverse dualism amounts to the evacuation of any power or objective function for divinity and the sacred that were the ultimate realities or reference points in all previous cosmologies. In the encapsulated mode they were within the cosmos, but still operated at the summit of the hierarchy, as a macrocosm which ruled and provided norms and meaning for the microcosm, the lesser realms of humans, animals, plants and the earth. In both the duality and the dualist modes, the sacred or the divine possessed similar functions.

Now, in reversed dualism this further dimension of the divine is absorbed into this, the one and only world, without even an internal hierarchy. This world therefore ceases to represent even a reversed dualism in any meaningful sense, and now requires a monistic cosmology. Everything, including our constructions both of a cultural religion and of a cultural science, is now in our own hands, within the ecological limits of our earthly environment. This is probably the first time in human history for the promulgation of such a thorough-going system – even the Indian monisms from the Axial Age allowed some relative if temporary reality, and some inherent structure, to the things of this world. These were not entirely at the mercy of our own constructive activities.

Beyond Cosmologies to Nihilism

The advent of postmodern philosophy in Western culture has exposed the unavoidable instability of such a truncated monistic cosmology. Hosts of analysts identify a postmodern future in terms of increasing plurality and variety in beliefs and behaviour, the advocacy of multi-cultural forms, each in its own right and with parity among them all, and a corresponding variety and parity of lifestyles and ethical codes among individuals. This is inevitable when there is no common, objective reference point that can present some degree of shared truth, with an authority that overrules our whims and preferences.

The extent to which postmodernism is radical in its break with the past was indicated when Michael Polanyi described his great book *Personal Knowledge* (1958) as "towards a post-critical philosophy", meaning post-Cartesian, post-Kantian, and post-Enlightenment. In 1990 the German Catholic theologian, Hans Küng, listed current signs that we live in the 'post' era. Our contemporary world is post-colonial, post-imperial, post-socialist, post-industrial, post-patriarchal, post-ideological, and post-confessional or denominational.[6]

To this formidable break with the familiar past, we could add post-traditional, post-Christendom, post-charismatic, post-ecumenical, post-liberal, post-welfare state; indeed we seem to be post-history itself, cut off from all roots. Or if a semblance of roots is needed, then back in 1949 George Orwell's *1984* depicted governments with an army of civil servants constantly rewriting every historical document to support their current and ever-changing political purposes. This would seem to be the last stage of a rootless culture, that rejects its past, and even the objective dimensions of its present, so that it reaches the ultimate stage of being post-reality, post-everything.

This inevitably recalls the last of Shakespeare's Seven Ages of Man: the "Last scene of all, that ends this strange eventful history, in second childishness, and mere oblivion, sans teeth, sans eyes, sans taste, sans everything."[7] Cultural analysts who pursue the implications further predict increasing fragmentation of a society released from any bonds outside itself, and the collapse of cultures and all cosmologies into the nihilism that Nietzsche, prophesied – 'sans everything'.

Nearly a century later, Jacques Monod expressed the same outlook in existentialist terms:

> Man must wake out of his millenary dreams, and discover his total solitude, his fundamental isolation. He must realise that, like a gypsy, he lives on the boundary of an alien world; a world that is deaf to his music, and as indifferent to his hopes as it is to his sufferings and his crimes...Who then is to define crime? Who decides what is good and what is evil?...Now he is master of (values) they seem to be dissolving in the uncaring emptiness of the universe.[8]

To help us grasp this long cultural process in Western history in another way, the foldout diagram at the end of the book summarizes the whole historical process. From the original unitive tribal era, through the earlier dualisms of antiquity to the 18th century Enlightenment that began reversing the dualism and produced the subsequent culture of modernity, and then into the reversed dualisms of 20th century postmodernity, leading to forms of monism that collapse into nihilism and anarchy – 'sans everything'.

The Power of the Image

Lest this appear unduly gloomy and too theoretical, let me illustrate the collapse from one of the current triumphs of technology, known as 'virtual reality'. In the audio-visual media it is possible to create the illusion of being involved with full three-dimensional reality for any scenario we like to conjure up, and even to the extent of being unable readily to detect the illusion, to distinguish the 'virtual' from the actual reality. In another area, convincing photographs can now be composed on a computer to any design, without any reference to the reality they pretend to present. The potential for deceit and manipulation is terrifying. But through another technological skill this deceit and manipulation are already sufficiently common to require legislation banning subliminal manipulation of our minds in our ordinary TV programmes.

What matters is not what is really happening to us, but what we think is happening, or what we can be brought to believe about so-called reality. We are into the era of the created and manipulated image that can float free from reality itself. Advertising depends increasingly on creating the desirable image; politicians employ public relations experts to remodel their public image for the media, starting with their hairstyle and the size of their grin – never mind leadership qualities, policies and grasp of the real world.

And even churches adopt the same deceits; several in New Zealand in recent years have reported decisions to smarten up their public image. What matters is not what truth and power they really do have to offer. When they are short on these they turn to what the public want and can be made to believe the churches can supply. There is no essential, hard-core item to purchase, or real person to vote for, or revealed divinity to worship. To all of which C.S. Lewis long ago replied prophetically in his *Mere Christianity*: "...you will never make a good impression...until you stop thinking about what sort of impression you are making."

The postmodern image-world is therefore an imaginary world which has no assured place for the religion and science we have been examining, or for truth itself. All can be created to suit those who have control of the technology, or the will to manipulate others. Society then collapses into a naked struggle for power by groups or individuals, freed from any control by shared truths they have not themselves created for their own ends. To control one's own controls is no control at all.

Again, Nietzsche saw it all a hundred years ago: the Age of Reason, that Enlightenment leaders thought they were introducing, becomes the Age of Power, of victory to the strongest and the smartest. We are in the age of the image, and the name of the image is power. This is the end product of this new form of a monistic cosmology. Likewise, it is the end of science as conveying the truth about reality, and the beginning of its prostitution to the selfish service of the most aggressive among us, which can only extend the kind of legitimate criticism of science as an instrument of power with which we have long been familiar.

The Source of Meaning

In answer to these critiques, and all this subjectivity, fragmentation and final collapse, we are offered new shared meanings for life in this sole, real world, meanings that 'faith' will be able to construct in this 'new age'. It is true that an important function of religion, both implicitly in the tribal era, and quite explicitly in the more reflective Axial religions and in the Greek philosophers, is to provide a meaning for the world and our lives upon it. This function must now be taken over from the increasingly defunct tribal and Axial religions, and assumed by the new religion that we create for a scientific world.

This could be called the central theme of Lloyd Geering's *Tomorrow's God*. He first sets out how he thinks we create our own 'worlds' or versions of 'reality'. Then he finds meaning for these from the religions that we also have to create to provide this meaning – DIY with a vengeance. Let me quote from the final paragraph of the book as providing a representative statement of this viewpoint:

> If we choose to speak of God, we shall be using this term to focus on all that we supremely value and on the goals which make human existence meaningful and worthwhile; and there is no place where we do not encounter this God. All reality is nothing less than 'the body of God'... This God is in the physical earth of which we are a tiny part. Even more, this God is to be found in all living creatures. Most of all, this God is rising to self-awareness in the (as yet) confused collective consciousness of the global human community. This is tomorrow's God, calling us from a world yet to be created. But, to create this world, this God...has no plan for the future except what we plan.[9]

Our only, if rather pious, comment is: May God save us from searching in a circle for such a feeble and undeveloped, inhuman god. But in his schema there is no such rescue. This one revealing paragraph invites a host of comments on its return to a sacralized universe, and especially from one who has shown such understanding of the de-sacralizing processes in the Hebraic world. Here there is a pantheism more extreme and depersonalized than in the tribal cultures; there is the 'logic' of such a depersonalized god actively 'calling', and doing so from 'a world yet to be created'; and there is the total abandonment of the Hebraic prerequisites that we have identified as essential for the development of science. It is impossible to see how in such a world there could be any science to raise the question of its relation to religion.

But I shall concentrate on the question of meaning that is important for us all, and on its proposed source. Here meaning is presented not as something that we find in the universe, or that is given to us, but as something provided by the religions we create, and so as itself ultimately our own creation. In the end, therefore, I have the meaning I give myself – whatever this can mean.

That this process has no meaning derives from the simple fact that the meaning of anything must come from outside itself. Not even a cosmos can contain or provide its own meaning for those who are part of it. Archimedes had the equivalent in mechanics – 'give me a place to stand, and I will move the earth' – give me a fulcrum outside the world and my lever could move it.

One could explore this in terms of modern philosophy and quote Wittgenstein, or in mathematics and expound Gödel's theorem that no mathematical system is self-contained and can prove itself. Just as experience is *experience of something else*, and not just experience of experience; or as a symbol is a *symbol of something else*, to which it refers, and is not a symbol of either itself or of myself – so also neither the cosmos, nor any part of it, is the meaning of itself. The independent source for the meaning of anything, large or small, is almost a truism in modern thought.

A bicycle, therefore, does not find its meaning by any study of the materials of which it is made, or of their arrangement. Nor is it explained as a means of providing employment in the factory that made it. Its meaning appears only when the rider, something quite outside the bicycle, turns up and rides off.

Likewise, the moon gets its meaning as a satellite from its relation to the earth; the meaning of parenthood emerges from the children; the meaning of your life and my life is found in the people, the institutions, the work, we have been involved with.

Meaning involves a transcending relationship to something else, because that is the interlocking way the universe is made. One version of how meaning comes from outside lies in what I once had drilled into me from the Westminster Shorter Catechism – and to my profit: "What is man's end? Man's chief end is to glorify God and enjoy Him for ever."

In another dimension there was the occasion when I had been driven south from Dunedin to Gore by night, and so I had no clear sight of the roads entering the town. Next day, in the late afternoon, I was being driven back north to Dunedin. But I became increasingly uneasy in a subconscious way; were we on the right route? The much younger driver was highly intelligent and experienced. I must keep quiet and not fuss as a nervous or know-all oldie. And then I saw that the sun setting in the west was on our right, whereas if we were going north to Dunedin it would be on our left. We were in fact several miles on our way in the wrong direction. But it took the check from the sun, a reference point right outside the immediate context, to show the true meaning of what we were doing.

Even the scholarly students of meaning in the new science of semiotics have to look beyond their own analyses in terms of 'the secret meanings of everyday life', to use the sub-title of Jack Solomon's book. These hidden meanings reveal the search for power, in cultures and in individuals, and the supporting ideologies. After illuminating accounts of what often lies behind the image, the book concludes by declaring "what semiotics is all about: the power we have to define and enforce our own conceptions of reality."[10] This would seem to be a harsher and more realistic version of creating our own worlds. But the book's final two sentences undermine this self-understanding: "In the end, this book itself is a sign whose meaning fits into an entire cultural system. Now what might that meaning be?"[11]

The form of this conclusion might be somewhat whimsical, but it is entirely correct in suggesting that the answer to semiotics' search for meaning has in the end to be sought elsewhere, beyond that cultural enterprise.

I am, therefore, satisfied that new and radical form of encapsulation, the closed and isolated 'faith's new cosmos', lacking any further reference point either within it or without, it is this itself which is devoid of meaning, and moves to its collapse in the course of a struggle for power. In this scenario both science and religion, as they impress upon us realities beyond us, these are the victims. Their constructed replacements have no continuity with what we have called science or religion, or in fact with anything else; they are indeed post-science and post-religion in a postmodern age – post everything!

Return to Reality:
Science and Theology in Partnership

Let me now say that this pessimistic view is in itself an outdated construction that has lost relation to what was really happening in our world at the end of the 20th century. The deepest understanding of our culture and our world at this stage of history is much more encouraging. This is revealed when we take the long look over three or four millennia and identify the four cosmologies that have emerged, and the relations between them. We then discover the scientific bankruptcy of the continuing tribal and Axial faiths, the neglected duality cosmology of the Hebrew people, and the intimate historical relation of the subsequent Judaeo-Christian worldview with the emergence of science. There is here a firmly historical and newly discovered basis for what I shall now present.

With this equipment we can now understand the connection between what Herbert Butterfield called the two greatest movements in history: (1) the Hebrew-Christian movement that we have followed from about 2000 BCE to the early centuries of the Common Era, depositing creeds and doctrines establishing the real nature of the cosmos. (2) The modern scientific movement focussed on the 16th and 17th centuries, offering laws and formulations about the behaviour of this cosmos, outshining everything since the rise of Christianity, reducing the Renaissance and Reformation to the rank of mere episodes, and transforming the whole diagram of the physical universe.[1] Those who work within the Frazer/Geering schema can call this "the greatest revolution in human civilization that there has ever been."[2] This ignores the earlier revolution above, which we would identify as even more fundamental than the second, for the latter in a sense is but an outworking of the first.

The Many Factors in the Rise of Science

In affirming that this historical connection is more than the happenstance that some have seen, but rather an integral relationship, I do not want to claim too much. If I say that the duality cosmology was an essential but not a sufficient cause then room is left for other factors. These can include various Greek contributions: from sheer curiosity about the world to the very idea of rational, scientific explanation; specific ideas that either anticipated later scientific conclusions or were congruent with them; and the indirect stimulus of Aristotelian science that clashed with the Hebraic cosmology. This forced the early Christian theologians working away at their doctrine of creation, to refute the reigning Greek systems, and incidentally to illustrate the cross-fertilization that exists between theology and science that we shall shortly consider further.

Room is also left for the contributions of certain intellectual and educational institutions, such as the Alexandrian academies (by no means all Christian) or the first European universities (by no means all orthodox or freed from Aristotelianism). In addition, and perhaps more basic, is the general milieu that science seems to require – a certain level of civilization and of economic development, and suitable social structures and technologies, all of which were to be found in western Europe at the appropriate times. And then there is always the unpredictable factor of the individual, such as Philoponus, Buridan and others, and especially in the 16th and 17th centuries, the 'men for the times'.

Those with an inbuilt reluctance to credit the Judaeo-Christian factor with anything so important as the rise of science reduce it to a somewhat incidental context, a 'happenstance' for the operation of these other apparently secular influences.

To do so is to overload them with specific scientific contributions they were unable to make, but that we have identified in the particular scientific themes on which the Christian thinkers worked. To shift the focus to these other factors not only overloads them but also forgets that many of these also arose in a Christian milieu, and to some extent at least were themselves the products of the Judaeo-Christian society and worldview.

Beyond De-sacralization to Dualism or Duality?

There are those who agree with much of the above, and are prepared to declare that "there is a direct correlation between the de-sacralization of the natural world and the rise of the modern scientific enterprise. Modern science evolved in the Western world instead of elsewhere as an indirect consequence of Christian culture...the reason why was the fundamental distinction it made between the domains of the sacred and the profane."[3] These are acknowledged to be benefits from the dualistic worldview.

The assertion of a 'direct correlation' would seem to correspond to our 'essential relationship'. The problem then is how to maintain this important correlation with the Hebraic de-sacralization of the world, while placing the consequent Judaeo-Christian faith in the dualist Axial category. This arises from failure to see that de-sacralization is only the first, preparatory step, and that it is the subsequent attitude towards this de-sacralized world that is critical – whether this be negative or positive.

On the one hand, there were the negative views of the Axial, dualist faiths, depreciating this secular realm as lower, shadowy or less real. On the other hand and at the same time, the opposite, Hebraic, duality form of de-sacralizing was already appreciating the secular as good, and with a place in its Creator's purposes. We have now followed some of the implications of the widespread and disastrous failure to identify this crucial difference.

Science and Theology in Mutual Support

With the essential historical relation between science and the Judaeo-Christian tradition now sufficiently established, we may ask: What of their present and future relationship? Both are now challenged by the attempted reversions to the earlier encapsulated world that we have already examined, and by the search for spirituality that easily reverts to a dualist depreciation of the world of science. Only the duality cosmology can both keep the secular world properly secular, and maintain a full appreciation of its goodness, its rationality and its potential – which stand among the prerequisites for science.

Even more menacing is the postmodern attack on the very idea of truth, not only in religion (as with the Enlightenment and modernity) but now from within science itself. The question of the existence and the criteria of truth or knowledge belongs to the sphere of epistemology, the theory of knowledge, that lies neighbour to the cosmological issues upon which we are concentrating throughout. It deserves a similar historical treatment, from the Greeks to the present century, and this would reveal the epistemological form of the same dualism that has haunted the history of cosmology. This would affect science most severely in the centuries between the French philosopher, Descartes, who initiated its influential modern forms, through the late 18th century German philosopher Immanuel Kant to the start of the 20th century.

We cannot do justice to these issues here, and must rest content with saying that relativity and quantum physics have wrought a revolutionary change in our view of the nature of scientific knowledge. They have brought the observed object and the observing subject together in the process of knowing, and this has removed dualist views separating the 'facts out there' from the human mind 'inside here'. This has happened without collapsing the real world out there into a subjective creation of my own mind, as Michael Polanyi and others have been showing since the mid-century.[4]

This brings the view of knowledge in science into a format very similar to that in the Judaeo-Christian scriptures. Here knowledge of God is seen in terms of the highly personal interaction between ourselves, the knowers, and God, the known, which can equally be seen as the interaction between God the knower and ourselves the known. God is not 'a fact out there' for me to know 'in here'; nor am I a 'fact out there' to be known in the mind of God. Knowledge arises in the course of an interpersonal, interactive, mutual relationship. Neither God nor ourselves is collapsed into the mind of the other; as of course God is collapsed into the human mind for much of modernity and both God and the objective world are collapsed for the post-modernist.[5]

Science and theology therefore face the same threats, and can present very similar defences of how they seek the truth. This partnership is rein-forced if each discovers its historical roots – science in the Hebraic cosmology wherein its relative autonomy is preserved, and the Christian tradition in the cultural and religious revolution that escaped from the encapsulated world and yet avoided the false Axial, dualist alternatives. They are cognate developments within the same worldview.

Science and Theology in Mutual Fertilization

With this mutual understanding science and the theology of the Christian religion are free to enter into mutual stimulation and the cross-fertilization of ideas. This will sound strange to those reared on belief in their inherent conflict, but after our survey it should be more understandable. This was what A.N. Whitehead glimpsed as happening in the carryover from rational theologizing in the Middle Ages to rational thinking in science. The burden of our historical survey of individual theologians working on the doctrine of creation and finding there clues for the critique of Greek science has been exactly this cross-fertilization, in times when scientific and theological thinking had not suffered their later sad separations.

As another example we can turn to the one whom Einstein regarded as the real father of the revolution in physics, James Clerk Maxwell (1831-79). As I have written elsewhere, this Scot "spent his Sundays studying theology, seeking to relate his religion and his science. His foundational contribution to the coming physics revolution was the rejection of the atomistic Newtonian theory of matter interacting at a distance, and the exploration of a *relational* view of realities constituted by *dynamic relations* within a common field (I speak as a layman). This dramatic change came not from scientific reasoning but from a mind stored with the Christian theology of a *relationally*-constituted godhead with *dynamic relations* between its trinitarian members, and a similarly *dynamic relationship* with its own creation – and stimulated by Faraday's experiments. This means that basic structures in his theology and his science began to match, and he had assimilated them from his theology before he began to pursue them in his science."[6]

This matching and interaction of concepts and the exploration of analogies is now being more consciously pursued by both scientists and theologians, and especially so within the relational views both of how all existence is constituted and of how it is known. It is not surprising that the extensive new work on the relationality within the Trinity since Karl Barth in the mid-20th century should resonate with the exploration of a relational structure for matter. The Christian doctrine of creation has stressed the presence of the image of a relationally-natured God, not only in the relation of male and female as in Genesis 1:27, but also in the rationality and order of creation as a whole.

It is therefore not irrelevant to explore at least the analogy between the Trinity and the phenomenon of the 'triple point' in physics. Water, for example, under certain precise conditions of pressure and temperature, enters a triple state wherein it simultaneously and continuously passes to and fro from liquid to solid to gaseous forms, each of which is really 'water', and yet has its own identity. The analogy with the simultaneous trinitarian nature of the godhead is obvious. Likewise the two forms of light, wave and particle, suggest analogies with the two natures, divine and human, of Jesus; these are equally real and simultaneously operative, and yet we cannot fully focus on both at the same time.[7]

Then again there are the familiar objections to the claims of uniqueness for Jesus Christ, and for a unique role for the Hebrew people in divine revelation. 'How odd of God to choose the Jews' – indeed how unjust to all other peoples; and so there is the 'scandal of particularity', and especially of claims to truth for the unique incarnation. This objection forgets that all history consists of particularities, and overlooks the 'unfair' fact that TV (and almost everything else) was invented in one place and enjoyed by a few people before others. And now modern physics is full of fascinating singularities, as they are called – from the particular speed of light, and the odd expansion of water when frozen, to the very particular rate of expansion of the universe after the Big Bang, so that it neither went too fast and so blew entirely apart, nor went too slowly so that gravitational forces would collapse it back to its original condensed state – it was fine-tuned for the one right speed.[8]

T.F. Torrance has well put the interaction between singularity in theology and in physics: "...the concept of singularity has bounced back...and has been radically transforming scientific thinking...singularity is now no longer an idea abhorrent to science, but...a proper scientific concept of absolutely central importance...it has become the great rock of offence upon which the old Enlightenment idea of science...of universal timeless laws has shattered itself, for the universal and the concrete particular have come together... [Now] scientists are open to the absolute singularity of the incarnation, which they had hitherto rejected...because it was a singularity. The whole intellectual climate has changed."[9]

These unique physical specificities are of course but manifestations of the essential contingency of the creation that we have earlier described as of crucial importance for the possibility of science. None could have been discovered by deductive reasoning from first principles, either theological or physical; they awaited detailed scientific research. I am not suggesting that either the divine or the scientific phenomenon proves the truth of the other. We must always remember the saying that 'the theology that marries the science of today may find itself a widow tomorrow.' This applies to relationships at the level of changing scientific views and theories rather than at the deeper levels of basics and epistemology with which we are here concerned.

At this level the contingency factor in all knowledge, as well as our human finitude, 'fallenness' and fallibility are particularly applicable. It is therefore impossible to expect too close a correlation between science and theology, or at all points; each must have some elbow room and relative independence. At the same time, modern developments in the biological sciences are raising urgent questions in the new field of bio-ethics that quickly lead into basic theological issues. There is therefore no simple formula for either separating or relating science and theology. Our basic thesis, however, remains true: that in the first place they can illumine one another, and that in the second place, if all truth is one, and if the created world does reflect its Creator, then something like this common pattern is the least we can expect.

These various relations – historical, supportive, and cross-fertilizing – provide unexpected rejections of the popular and traditional stereotypes, and of the Frazer/Geering schema. Despite all the threats of the postmodernist, both the present situation and the future open out into what might best be called 'Truth's New Age'. Reality has a way of having the last word, and not least when it is being most strenuously ignored.

Three 20th Century Cosmology Changes

We are therefore more prepared to recognise the true significance of the 20th century in relation to the great cultural changes identified with science in the past, and especially in terms of cosmology. T.F. Torrance has set forth three such changes, and named them from the leading individuals involved. The first was Ptolemaic cosmology from the second century of our common era, which epitomized Greek science and established a deep split, a radical dualism, in the cosmos between the rational and therefore intelligible realm of celestial realities and the everyday realm of earthly phenomena. This was the antagonist of the duality cosmology right through until the 20th century escape from dualism.

The second great mutation was the Newtonian cosmology from the 16th century, recognised as the birth of modern science, but still infected with the dualist separation of mind and matter both in its cosmology and in its theory of knowledge, and with Copernicus, Galileo and Descartes still hindered by the 'correct' Aristotelian systems. This same dualism was extended by the Enlightenment and still persists in the now outdated 'modernity' outlook. The achievements of modern science are all the more remarkable when we see they have occurred in spite of this continuing handicap.

The third great mutation in the scientific outlook of Western culture is the revolution embodied in the 20th century Einsteinian cosmology. We have only begun to benefit from all that this implies. For one thing, it is the end of the three cosmologies we have identified – the encapsulated view with its pantheism and modern revivals, the Axial Age and Greek views with their persistent dualisms, and the implied monisms that are the end-product of postmodernism. These alternatives are now transcended as we explore the transition from the analytic era in science with its mechanistic ideas, to the new synthetic or relational era with a more dynamic view of the universe.[10]

Similar Theological Changes

Alongside these three cosmological milestones we may place the corresponding theologies. The Ptolemaic system was integrally related to a Greek theology that was simply wrong, and it provoked the theological response of the early Christian fathers with a doctrine of creation that contained the lineaments of both theological and scientific truth, culminating in a Philoponus. These positions, however, were to be overtaken by the rediscovery of classical culture in the Middle Ages and had to struggle for existence, and for further development, as we have seen above.

The Newtonian cosmology was therefore bedevilled by this inheritance of Greek science with its theological implications, and by the infiltration that these had made into mediaeval theology, especially in the great system of Thomas Aquinas. Theology was not sufficiently governed by incarnational and trinitarian criteria as in the early creeds. This is apparent in the theological writings of Kepler, and especially in the dualist Arian or unitarian theology of Newton himself.

Only in the 20th century, as the Einsteinian cosmology has unfolded, was there a corresponding, profound, theological, paradigm change. From the mid-20th century there was a revival of interest in patristic studies of the early Christian centuries, and their relevance to modern science is a new discovery. Then the giant figure of the Swiss theologian, Karl Barth (1886-1968), presented a massive relational and trinitarian critique of the theologies that developed under the influence of the Cartesian philosophy of Descartes and the associated Enlightenment philosophy of Kant.

Every major theologian since Barth has worked and published on the Trinity. And it is no accident that one of the chief disciples and exponents of Barth and of the early Christian fathers, theologian T.F. Torrance of Edinburgh, should be engaged in bridging the gap between science and theology, and in the course of this be elected as the only lay member of the prestigious European Institute of Physics. The effects of these developments, however, have not yet visibly worked through to the churches, much less to the public. But this is where the real action lies in the theological world, and not in the marginal activities of the Don Cupitts and the Bishop Spongs on their outdated fronts.

Truth's New Age

The true excitement about our new age, therefore, has nothing to do with remodelling Christianity and the Axial Age religions so that they can survive as human creations providing 'faith' in a scientific age; rather exactly the reverse. It has everything to do with eliminating this false trail so that we can attend to the real frontiers of science. Then we can surprise ourselves by discovering their relation to the frontiers of theology in 20th century incarnational and trinitarian studies. This congruence is then explained through the interwoven histories of science and of theology that have led us back to their origins in a duality cosmology over three millennia ago.

For the first time in the whole history of Western culture and of Christianity, both science and theology have simultaneously been freed from the incubus of the dualisms that invaded from the East. This makes our era truly epoch-making in the whole sweep of human cultural history, for it brings to fruition that first epoch-making Hebraic move into a view of the universe where Creator and creation are clearly distinguished while remaining in positive, open, contingent and free interaction.

The irony of our age is the attempt of members of an exhausted and confused culture to find revival by looking to the East for wisdom and power – whether by the trek of Western youth to India with its Axial religions, or the Western response to imported Eastern gurus and cults. The running battle through three millennia between dualist and duality cosmologies is not over, as witness also the fanciful contortions of postmodernism. But the Hebraic cosmology is being articulated and equipped in both its scientific and its theological dimensions as never before, and if in the end power lies with the truth, and reality does have the last word, then we can believe that we are indeed participating in the birth of 'Truth's New Age'.

A POLANYIAN EPILOGUE

Michael Polanyi, very early in his concern with the epistemological question of truth, wrote a letter to the British scientific journal *Nature*, that will be almost unknown. For Polanyi, then not long back from visiting Stalinist Russia, the visible antagonist in the struggle was the Marxist ideological construction of 'truth' in the sciences. Now the Marxist antagonist has collapsed, and has been replaced by the new constructivisms in our own societies, bearing the labels of cultural relativity, multi-culturalism and postmodernism. Polanyi would have recognised them.

His excursions into congruent biblical analogies for his epistemology indicate that he would also agree with our statement if we were to substitute throughout the word 'theology' for his 'science'. Theology also must be controlled by the passionate search for truth, in its own proper data and by its own appropriate methods, and not by the demand for relevance to changing social concerns, cultural categories and other extraneous factors. Those who can recognise that science and theology share the same struggle for the truth, and who therefore recognise the thrust of this epilogue, will have understood the subject of this essay, and appreciate the following words of Polanyi:

...I can recognise nothing more holy than scientific truth...Science exists only to the extent to which the search for truth is not socially controlled. And therein lies the purpose of scientific detachment. It is of the same character as the independence of the witness, of the jury, of the judge; of the political speaker and the voter; of the writer and teacher and their public; it forms part of the liberties for which every man with an idea of truth and every man with a pride and dignity of his soul has fought since the beginning of society. The struggle today is at its height...[11]

Provocative Postscript

This investigative journey through the world's religions has discovered the roots of science to lie within the worldview of one of these religions, the Judaeo-Christian tradition. Since the search has been conducted at the basic philosophical and theological levels of cosmology, its results have a finality and ultimacy that can be questioned only by further historical and analytic work at the same levels. To upset our conclusions, it would have to be shown that both the expert Joseph Needham and my much less expert self are wrong in our judgment of the relation of Chinese civilization to science; that we are wrong in our account of the ambiguous Greek achievements and of the contribution of Philoponus to the necessary overthrow of Aristotelianism; that we are mistaken in the significance given to the Hebrew de-sacralization of the creation; that there was no truth in the new importance given to the medieval period by Duhem and Whitehead; in short that, at these and other key points, our basic thesis will not survive scholarly examination.

I recognize that much of what I have said may need further refinement or qualification by those expert in different areas of the wide field we have covered. Nevertheless we stand by the broad picture and the thesis that have emerged. Those who have not made such a journey before may well find its conclusions clashing with their own settled convictions. A basic treatment such as this will necessarily have implications at other levels, and for many current issues.

The adjective applied to this postscript is used in one of the positive senses of the verb 'provoke' – to allure, or call forth. We therefore hope to instigate further investigation by listing some of these implications. We have had to challenge historical stereotypes (about the Greeks, and the Middle Ages), fashions of thought (especially in the media), cultural assumptions, and ideologies that defend ingrained attitudes and vested interests. In sum, it has been necessary to go against the stream of much modern and post-modern Western culture and the prevailing currents in many other cultures, as well as to fill in certain gaps in our knowledge, such as those connected with Philoponus and Duhem.

The Scandal of Particularity

A major problem for many will probably lie in the singling out of the Judaeo-Christian tradition as the necessary basis for science (seen as true knowledge in its own spheres), and by implication as itself the one true religion. This also implies a certain uniqueness for Western culture which has been so identified with both science and the Christian faith. Conversely we have set forth how the tribal faiths and the great Axial religions of Asia and their cultures neither did nor could have produced modern theoretical science. It seems arrogant and scandalous to make such a claim in the modern multi-faith and multi-culture world.

This objection is quite irrational when one considers that this 'scandal of particularity' applies to most of the facts of history in their uniqueness. To find the roots of science in the tribal people of a single small country like Palestine, and its full development within the Christian context of Western Europe, is no exception to the nature of history. Those who object to this as a 'scandalous' claim are quite prepared to ignore the scandal of geometry being developed in the one small country of ancient Greece, and focussed on the one person of Euclid. History is made up of such singular advances into the truth of things.

I shall allow myself the satisfaction of a more local example. Mt Everest was scaled for the first time by a New Zealand beekeeper called Edmund Hillary and a Nepalese mountaineer called Tensing. They were chosen for the final assault from the members of a highly skilled team of climbers. Others ambitious for the task might have been chosen for this prestigious act, and have been equally successful. But the leader, John Hunt, selected these two, as an act of judgement, and not even he knew in advance who the final pair would be. The history of Everest's conquest has taken this particular course, Hillary was knighted, and New Zealand added to its list of achievements. Subsequently there has arisen what can be called the Everest movement, with its conquerors running into hundreds from every race, age and culture.

The very ordinariness of this example makes the point about the course of history with its particularities. It also applies to an insignificant figure called Abraham who with his fellow-tribalists first began to diverge from the worldwide unitive cosmology towards the new duality worldview. When finally adopted by the Hebrew people, and developed into the doctrine of creation of the first worldwide faith, this made science possible. 'How odd of God, to choose the Jews', runs the limerick; but it would have been really odd indeed to have contradicted the historical processes built into the Creator's own creation and now recognized across the world as the normal way of things. Abraham and Sir Edmund Hillary each illustrate the unexpected particularities of history.

It is highly significant that these features of history correspond to what are known as the singularities of science, the apparently odd but in fact critically exact dimensions of many physical phenomena. Often quoted is the particular known speed at which the 'Big Bang' occurred, neither too slow so that its products were drawn back by gravitational force to their original position, nor so fast that they scattered into outer space beyond any possibility of forming a recognizable universe. A simpler example is the singular behaviour of water, to expand when it freezes. This special 'particularity' is a kind of 'scandal' in relation to the behaviour of the other elements, which behave 'properly' by shrinking on cooling. Without this scandal, ocean ice would not float but sink to the bottom, and the oceans would gradually freeze to the top; life on an earth would be impossible amid oceans of solid ice. And so on with all the other singularities built into the behaviour of the physical creation. History and physics find these particularities no scandal but see them as vital features built into their fields.

Among objections raised to our particular thesis about the origins of science, there is the happenstance theory of John Hick and others – that science was ready to develop and did so only in Western Europe because of the fortuitous conjunction of favourable factors, social, economic and political. There was no integral relation with the Christian faith, nor any theoretical dependence on its doctrines. 'Ready to develop' and 'fortuitous' then become merely superficial stop-gap terms, masking a refusal to explore the actual history of this 'readiness' and this favourable conjunction, as we have done. This flight from available knowledge if applied elsewhere would render historical study useless, and ultimately make history itself meaningless – as no more than an inexplicable conjunction of happenstances!

Demeaning History's Achievements and Religions

It would seem that some do not *want* this historical account of science and religion to be true. One can understand this on the part of a devoted Classicist who finds that 'the glory that was Greece', its literature, drama, sculpture, architecture, philosophy and indeed its scientific beginnings, are being tarnished by our critiques, especially of the great Aristotle. This is not so. I once taught a university course on Aristotle's ethics, and I rejoice at the renewed interest today in something like his ethics of virtue. But it is possible for a great culture to be magnificently wrong at key points and in spite of this to make splendid contributions to human history. Otherwise there would be no room for the mixture of truth and error that marks us all, together with our cultures. Once again there would be no room for real history.

Similar comment applies to Western Sinologists and still more to Chinese scholars who explore the amazing technical achievements of Chinese civilization and its forays into scientific theory, and then feel betrayed from within by a Joseph Needham who admits that science was never to be born there.

Likewise for Islamists, both within and without that faith, who dwell on the achievements of Islamic peoples in medicine, architecture, art and mathematics, and then feel cheated when these are excluded from the theoretical foundations of science. We have already explained this, but another way might be to speculate on the history of science if Islam had crossed the Pyrenees and met up with fellow-believers who had broken through 'the gates of Vienna' to make all Western Europe an Islamic culture area.

I do not intend to demean important activities like those of the Centre for the Study of Islam and Christian Muslim Relations at the Selly Oak Colleges in Birmingham, England, or the numerous Councils for Christians and Muslims proliferating as Muslims increase in Western countries. I do, however, suggest that these activities will be distorted if conducted on the basis of an unexamined ideological view of the history of such a fundamental matter as science.

And so we could proceed for all the other cultures and religions, which, despite their acknowledged contributions, find they are described in Jaki's term as having reached an impasse when it comes to science itself. In no sense do we demean them, or regard their faiths as less than authentically religious; indeed we recognize that some have sustained whole civilizations through several millennia of the trials and tribulations of human life.

A New Place for the Tribal Religions

Our favourite expression of this respect for diverse religions concerns the Vodou religion of the people of Haiti. Many despise this as 'voodoo', a primitive, even dangerous superstition, but we prefer to see it as a faith that has sustained the mass of Haitians through two centuries of a most wretched history, even though it cannot be called 'true' or ever integrate with the scientific worldview.

My own study of Vodou occurred in the course of research into the new independent religious movements related to tribal cultures. In chs. 2 and 9 above I have shown how seriously I take both the original primal religion and the new interaction movements, no matter how far some of these may be from any recognizable Christian position. In no sense could I be said to demean either the tribal or the new movements. In fact I have played my part in the reversal of the earlier negative attitude towards them, and many of the latter provided unexpected evidence in support of my overall thesis.

It is possible to go even further and re-examine the common 'league table' of religions. In this the great monotheistic religions are placed at the top and those of the polytheistic or animist tribal peoples either at the bottom, or not even on the table at all – as in the *Oxford Companion to World Religions* which we have already exposed, and in other books on religions. These primal religions have escaped the dualisms of the Axials, and have made a massive response to Christianity, both in alliance with missions and independently.

Despite the difference in their respective cosmologies, they could be claimed to show an affinity with the Christian faith that is lacking in the Axials. If the Christian tradition offers a normative meaning for the word 'religion', and therefore presents its most authentic form, then this affinity suggests that the primals may be more authentically religious than the Axial faiths.

In short, the league table should be inverted as far as some of the Axials are concerned, and these should exchange places with the primals. One thinks of classic Buddhism which might still occupy an influential place in history as a philosophy or a psychology rather than as a religion – a suggestion that is supported by the way its popular level so readily passes over into folk forms of animism. This suggestion will seem shocking to many, but arises as one of the further and unexpected implications of our basic analysis of the cosmologies.

This 'rehabilitation' of primal religions must not be misinterpreted to support the current fashionable reversion to the primitive and the tribal seen in certain New Age developments that we described at the end of chapter 10. Nor should it give the wrong kind of encouragement to the new movement of Christian indigenous peoples that has spread from its Native American and Maori originators in the 1990s. If this movement is not to fall victim to the canonizing of the past of tribal peoples, it badly needs tools to both appreciate and yet critique the common religious and cultural heritages that it is recalling.

Inter-Faith Dialogue

In the 20th century, inter-faith dialogue has become a major activity between religious leaders, and has led to inter-faith organizations and services of worship. The reasons are obvious: the end of the Christian powers' colonial era; vastly increased information in the West about other faiths and a new aggressiveness on their part; the extension of the ecumenical attitude beyond the domestic Christian domain; and the large movements of other believers across traditional boundaries and into Western countries. This development has accelerated through the century and has been immensely supported by the pluralism and relativism of a postmodern culture, which encourages by-passing the question of common truth.

Dialogue then replaces confrontation, and Christian mission is transposed into development aid. The result in the popular mind is found in the widely used image of a mountain, with the various religions each providing a different route up to the common shared summit of religious truth, the divine or God. This is calculated to offend nobody and offer some praise to all. It must be a very rare mountain that can be climbed in this way, and the opposite was certainly true of the climbing of Mt Everest.

If theology seeks the ultimate truth about the Creator, and science does the same for the creation, then it is reasonable to expect some similarity in their history and their methods. Our work in this book is a detailed refutation of the many-roads-up-the-mountain image for the history of science; this discovered the only successful route by following the map of one particular cosmology developed within one particular culture and religious tradition.

Other cultures made forays up the mountain following different maps but all reached Jaki's impasses. They had to remain content with the technologies that were possible at the foot of the mountain, although some of the discoveries on their forays upwards proved to be essentials for the climb. These were taken up by those who did succeed in the end – some of the Greek mathematical and astronomy discoveries, and those concerned with the theory of numbers and of their notation that originated in China, India, or among the Arabs. These cross-cultural transfers, however, confirm the particularity written into the history of science, as it is of religions.

The roads-up-the-mountain image is, however, open to even more serious criticism. It assumes an uncritical and therefore a comprehensive parity of religions and cultures, as it would do also for parity between various local 'sciences'. This is ideological nonsense until it is broken up into *formal* parity and *content* disparity. All societies have their own authentic religions and cultures and in this respect are *formally equal* and deserve respect; we took Haitian Vodou as an extreme example. Cultural and religious *contents*, however, are *widely disparate* and can no more be equally true than are their disparate 'scientific' and cosmological beliefs.

More radical still is the critique that even the formal parity of religions that is implied in the climbing-the-mountain image does not include all religions. The Christian belief is not that this one faith has found the right route to the top, but that the divine has come down from the summit, as it were, and with the fullest respect for the particularities of historical life in the human realm, has dwelt within one particular society at one particular time and place. For this incarnation no special credit was due to the Hebrew people themselves; the normal processes of history were involved, and led to the developments we have surveyed with respect to science.

If this inversion of the mountain image is maintained by those in the Judaeo-Christian tradition there should be no arrogance or triumphalism about climbing techniques, altitudes reached, or glimpses gained of the summit, as compared with other religions. It is sufficient humbly to tell their different history as we have done here, to articulate their particular cosmology and follow through its implications for the history of science. Christians engaged in inter-faith dialogue who speak from any other basis are representing a modern ideological creation and not the faith in its historical form and distinctives.

Other Implications

The manifold further implications of our thesis can only be suggested here. These include a major revision of the academic teaching of theology to include in its doctrine of creation a biblical cosmology that leads into modern science and its history. Conversely, the history of science as commonly taught ignores the route we have travelled and makes no mention of many key figures in its theoretical development.

A doctrine of creation should also be able to develop an eco-theology and to dismiss the popular charge that societies within the Judaeo-Christian tradition are responsible for modern ecological problems. All living societies can be shown to have shared in the rape of the earth. The biblical cosmology not only supports the science that can fulfill the earth's potential, but provides protection against the negative attitudes towards it found in the Axial faiths and in all dualisms. It also protects against the opposite attitudes in the ecological movement, whereby the earth is re-sacralized in a mystical manner that reverts to a unitive tribal cosmology, prevents its proper development, and subverts science itself.

There are also profound implications for inter-cultural relations, since religions have lain at the heart of all cultures and science can no longer be escaped by any of them. All cultures and their worldviews now have to come to terms with what has happened within Western culture, and one reaction is seen in the extensive immigration from the traditional Axial religions areas of Asia into Western societies. Even when not promoted as in Australia and New Zealand, people in the non-Western societies are voting with their feet when able to make their own choices. Those who speak of parity of cultures or who denigrate Western culture have nothing to say to such as these.

Western governments and peoples ignore the deeper issues of this remarkable modern phenomenon. They remain satisfied with the superficial assimilation of immigrants whose deeply rooted worldviews are hostile to science, and who are therefore forced into a schizophrenic situation of which they are largely unconscious. They are attempting to live on the basis of two incompatible worldviews and this can only spell deep trouble ahead. We have, however, already traced how the Hebrew people effected a radical change in the cosmology of their worldview, while retaining its traditional expressions by reinterpreting them on another basis. This model can provide receiving countries with a profounder understanding of what is involved in the immigration process, and of the dangers of creating sub-cultures that are deeply incompatible with the host culture.

There are of course many within the Western receiving societies who are themselves alienated from the traditional roots, and who assume that they speak in the name of science when they reject all association with the Judaeo-Christian faith, or radically remodel it out of all historical recognition. We have mentioned the Frazer/Geering viewpoint, and have named other individuals; to these may be added the 'Jesus Seminar' group mainly in the USA and some of the popularizers of their versions of science, such as Carl Sagan, Stephen Hawking and Richard Dawkins.

I take the latter for a final comment because he has been so effectively answered from within science itself by a local colleague, Neil Broom, in his book, *How Blind Is the Watchmaker?*[1] and in an article entitled 'The Selfish Gene: a crude and naive fabrication'.[2] These refer to the titles of Dawkins' popular books, which attempt to account for human life, including even the appearance of science itself, 'in terms of an entirely material set of processes...that appear to make the neo-Darwinian view of life entirely believable.'

This total materialism takes the huge step of dispensing with all three types of cosmology associated with the cultures and religions within which our history has been set. This history then represents fabrications of the human mind irrelevant to the rise of science; but why such misleading history should develop is left unexplained. From within biology itself, Professor Broom exposes Dawkins' faulty logic and misuse of data, and then concludes:

> Neo-Darwinism...presents a gross trivialization of biological realities... The metaphors and images...are seriously misleading and serve only to disguise the much more fundamental teleological aspects that a purely naturalistic science is powerless to address. Neo-Darwinism is in urgent need of a major conceptual rethink.[3]

The editor of *The Ecologist* is still more critical in his introductory note to the above article: "Dawkins' neo-Darwinism merely reflects the extreme reductionism...of the aberrant, atomized and totally materialistic society we have created. It is of sociological interest only."[4]

This is a drastic way of stating that there is no contribution to science in Dawkins' books since they are controlled by an ideology in defence of his own personal rejection of any non-material factors, such as those involved in religions. This alternative worldview is an available option that reflects much in modern Western society, rather than research in biology or any other science, or into the history of science and the religions. As a worldview it has to compete with the different view that we have been using in providing a coherent account of this history.

The reader has to decide between them, and this postscript will have succeeded if, in the positive rather than the negative sense, it provokes further thought on issues fundamental to our Western culture, and to all other cultures and their joint future in this one world we all share.

E N D N O T E S

Preface

1   Samuel P. Huntingdon, *The Clash of Civilizations and the Remaking of World Order*, New York, Simon & Schuster, 1996. This broad analysis of the post-Cold War world situation by the doyen of American political scientists, with its nine major cultures and its detailed applications, has become an important discussion focus in the 1990s and is essential for multi-cultural discussions. My own major critique is that he takes inadequate account of the bridging functions of truth in all spheres, and especially of one scientific truth for all peoples; i.e., he neglects the thesis of this book and its relation to Western culture.

Chapter One

1   Christopher Lasch, *The Culture of Narcissism*, New York: W.W. Norton & Co., 1979, p.5.

2   Peter Lineham, 'History or Myth?', *Stimulus* (Wellington, N.Z.) 6(1), Feb. 1998, p.3.

3   M.Mahner and M. Bunge, 'Is Religious Education Compatible with Science Education?', in *Science & Education*, 5(2), April 1996, pp.101-23. See also professional philosopher Mary Midgley, 'Strange Contest: Science Versus Religion', in H. Montefiore (ed.) *The Gospel and Contemporary Culture*, London: Mowbray 1992, pp.40-57, on the wrong views of science in this unnecessary confrontation.

4   Lesslie Newbigin, *Foolishness to the Greeks. The Gospel and Western Culture*, London: SPCK; Grand Rapids: W.B. Eerdmans, 1986, pp.66-67. The whole of ch.4, 'What can We know? The Dialogue with Science', is an excellent compact survey of the relation between science and religion that complements our own detailed history.

5   Idem, p.66.

6   I recognize the confusion that can arise from such similar terms, and would welcome alternative suggestions.

Chapter Two

1   Examples of this worldview drawn largely from Sol Tax, World View and Social Relations in Guatemala, *American Anthropologist*, n.s., 43, 1941, pp.38-40.

2   Vitruvius Pollio, *Ten Books on Architecture*, London: Constable 1961, Book 3, pp.72-73.

3   A.C. Bouquet, *The Christian Faith and Non-Christian Religions*, Welwyn, Herts.: James Nisbet & Co., 1958, p.53.

4   W. Koppers, *Primitive Man and his World Picture*, London: Sheed & Ward, 1952, pp. 136-8.

5   R.H. Lowie, Religion in Human Life, *American Anthropologist*, 65,(3,1), 1963, pp.332-42.

6   From the translation by C.R. Markham, Andeans, in J. Hastings (ed.) *Encyclopaedia of Religion and Ethics*, Edinburgh: T.& T. Clark, vol.1, 1908, p.470b.

7   Idem, p.471a.

8   David Harper, 'A Radical View of Human Sexuality', *Affirm* (Christchurch, N.Z.) 5(1), 1997, p.18, quoting from Dennis Praeger, 'Why Judaism Rejected Homosexuality', *Mission & Ministry*, Summer 1995.

Chapter Three

1   J.B. Pritchard (ed.), *Ancient Near Eastern Texts Relating to the Old Testament*, Princeton University Press, 2nd. ed., 1955, pp.370-1.

2   The use of this irrational phrase persists and spreads even in academic circles. I cannot refrain from referring to the massive *The Oxford Dictionary of World Religions*, Oxford University Press 1997. When I contributed some 68 entries in the mid-1980s, it was to *The Oxford Companion to 'Religions of the World*. It was then shelved until revival in the 1990s and I did not notice the change in title. Now this is embarrassing since I was unknowingly promoted from 'contributor'

to 'consultant' and named on the title page, albeit as living in the wrong country! More serious is the almost total omission of the primal religions we have here been taking so seriously – except for one unsatisfactory entry on 'African Religions' lumped together, and one other on 'Oceanic Religions' that contains not a single fact about these religions! So much for the label 'Oxford' and its 'World Religions'; this is the common fate of the primals,when this unfortunate phrase rules.

3   See A.C. Bouquet, op. cit., pp.96-99, for a wide sampling of texts from twelve Axial religions, illustrating a remarkably wide consensus on the spiritualization of religion, by affirming the value of personal 'spiritual sacrifices' as against ritual material sacrifice.

4   Michael Polanyi, 'The Growth of Thought in Society', *Economica*, 8, Nov. 1941, p.450. See also letter, Cultural Significance of Science, in *Nature*, 147, 25 Jan. 1941, p.119. A critique of Polanyi as oversimplifying, and a historical reconstruction of how the distinction between science and technology might have developed in the early Stone Age are presented in a paper by Robin Hodgkin to the Polanyi conference in Sheffield in January 1998..

5   For brief account, see *Scientific American*, October 1993, p.76.

6   S.L. Jaki, *The Savior of Science*, Washington, D.C.: Regnery Gateway, 1988, p.23; other information on Egypt.from the same section, pp.22-26.

7   S.L. Jaki, *Science and Creation*, Edinburgh: Scottish Academic Press, rev. & enl. edn., 1986, p.70. Much other information on Egypt from the same source.

8   Idem, pp.77-78.

9   Christopher Dawson, *Progress and Religion*, 1929, repr. Peru, Illinois: Sherwood Sugden & Co., n.d.,(1992), p.116.

10 For the significance of Pythagorus in the history of the relations between science and theology see Margaret Wertheim, *Pythagorus' Trousers: God, Physics and the Gender Wars*, Times Books, 1996, and the review article by Nancey Murphey in *Books & Culture*, Sept.-Oct., 1996, p.11.

11 Idem, pp.17, 23.

12 Joseph Needham, *The Grand Titration*, 1969, repr. 1993, p.45.

13 Christopher Dawson, in his *Dynamics of World History*, (J.J. Molloy, compiler),

London/New York: Sheed & Ward,1957, p.119.

14 Idem, p.120, sundry quotations from Plato.

15 From article Stoics, *Encyclopaedia Britannica*, 1972, p.267.

Chapter Four

1   L.G. Geering, *Faith's New Age*, London: Collins, 1980, pp.289-90.

2   Diogenes Allen, *Christian Belief in a Postmodern World*, Louisville, Kentucky: Westminster/John Knox Press, 1989, pp.25-26.

3   Jeremy Begbie, *Music in God's Purposes*, Edinburgh: Handsel Press, 1988, p.9.

4   C.N. Cochrane, *Christianity and Classical Culture*, Oxford: The Clarendon Press, 1940, p.443.

5   Max Weber, *Ancient Judaism*, New York: Free Press, 1952, p.223.

6   Elizabeth Newman, Rethinking the Eucharist, *Ecumenical Review*, October 1993, p.459.

7   H.P. Nebelsick, 'God, Creation, Salvation and Modern Science', *Horizons in Biblical Theology*, 9(2), Dec. 1987, pp.89-90.

8   L.G. Geering, op. cit., p.290. The simple cyclic/linear options we present need qualification, especially outside the tribal cultures when applied to Greek/Hebrew views. For the work of Thorlief Boman in critique of, e.g., Oscar Cullmann and Peter Brunner, see H.P. Nebelsick, *Renaissance and Reformation*, Edinburgh: T. & T. Clark, 1992, pp.170-5.

9   For a full treatment of the nature and history of the synagogue, see my *From Temple to Meeting House: The Phenomenology and Theology of Places of Worship*. The Hague: Mouton 1979, pp. 96-105, and ch.14 for the later history, especially pp.295-302 on the adherence of Orthodox Jewry to the original forms, and the return to temple forms in Reform Judaism.

10 Weber, op. cit., p.394.

11 Weber, op. cit., p.5.

Chapter Five

1   For fuller account of the New Testament position and the early Christians, see my op. cit., ch.7, ch.8 sections 4-5, and ch.9 section 1.

2   New Zealand has a special interest in this history, for in 1995 Dr Joan Taylor, of religious studies at Waikato University, published the fruit of a decade's work on the archaeol-

ogy of Palestine – *Christians and the Holy Places; the Myth of Jewish-Christian Origins.* This was awarded the prize for the best recent book on the archaeology of Israel – and there are seven Israeli universities with large religious studies and archaeology departments.

3   H.P. Nebelsick, *Circles of God*, Edinburgh: Scottish Academic Press, 1985, pp.89-90.

4   Idem, p.91.

5   S.L Jaki, op. cit., p.168.

6   Idem, p.170.

7   C.B. Kaiser, *Creation and the History of Science*, London: Marshall Pickering; Grand Rapids: Eerdmans, 1991, p.43. And see pp.34-51 for detailed account of the influence of the biblical worldview on healing, medicine and related technologies, including Basil's famine relief work, up to the 12th century.

8   Idem, pp.19-20.

9   Quoted from Augustine's *Confessions* in Christopher Dawson *et al.*, *A Monument to St. Augustine.* New York: Dial Press, 1930 – my reference from Christina Scott, *A Historian and His World*, London: Sheed & Ward, 1984, p.99.

10   Jaki, op. cit., p.181. The whole section, pp.177-83, is a fine summary of Augustine's contribution.

11   Idem, p.192.

12   Quoted by Jaki in op. cit., p.184.

13   R. Dales, quoted by Kaiser, op. cit, p.23.

14   M. Cohen and I.E. Drabkin gave us perhaps the first available English translations from Philoponus in their *A Source Book of Greek Science*, in 1948. This source was used by Marshall Clagett in his *Greek Science in Antiquity*, 1952; and in 1962 Samuel Sambursky of the Weizman Institute of Science in Jerusalem, published *The Physical World of Late Antiquity* (New York: Basic Books), with a final chapter on Philoponus. Sambursky also has a useful summary of 'Philoponus' in the Collier-Macmillan *Encyclopedia of Philosophy* of 1967 and reprints. I am indebted to these sources and also to the summary versions in H.P. Nebelsick, C.B. Kaiser and S.L Jaki (op. cit., pp.185-7) as cited. The main source for discussions of his physics is now Richard Sorabji (ed.), *Philoponus and the Rejection of Aristotelian Science*, London: Duckworth 1987. Henry Chadwick has a detailed chapter on Philoponus as Christian theologian. For the rest some of

the chapter titles indicate the range of this great physicist: 'Infinity and the Creation', ''Philoponus' Commentary on Aristotle's Physics in the Sixteenth Century', 'Philoponus and the Rise of Preclassical Dynamics', 'Philoponus' Impetus Theory in the Arabic Tradition.'

15   Incidentally, attention should be drawn to the replacement in the 1990s of the popular stereotypes of Galileo's history, and his 'rehabilitation' by the Catholic Church. He was neither a martyr nor condemned as a heretic, and the debate was not science versus theology, but partly scientific and partly political in the struggle of the Catholic Church to maintain its authority against the Protestant challenge. For a reliable account of Galileo see Philip Sampson, Victim of Spin, *Third Way* (Harrow, Middlesex) 21(5), June 1998, pp.23-26, exposing this 'foundational myth of the modern world' which corrupts the history of science.

16   Jaki, *Science and Creation*, p.186.

17   Jaki, *The Relevance of Physics*, Edinburgh: Scottish Academic Press, (1966) new ed. 1992, p.414. Jaki is quoting Philoponus from his great rival and critic, Simplicius.

18   *The Origins of Modern Science*, London: Bell, 1949, p.8.

19   T.F. Torrance, concluding paragraph of a lecture on 'The Cognitive Interface of Theology and Science, with Reference to John Philoponus' at the Pascal Centre, Ontario, July 1998.

20   Nebelsick, op. cit., p.108.

21   See my 'Chalcedonian Parameters for a Christian Stance as Prolegomena to Dialogue', in D.B. Hamil and M. Rae (eds.) *Theological Fragments: Essays in Honour of Alan Torrance.* Dunedin: Lada Publications 1994, pp. 19-25, especially n2, p.20.

22   Michael Polanyi in sundry places, including *Personal Knowledge*, University of Chicago Press, 1958 and later reprints, ch.13; *The Tacit Dimension*, London: Routledge & Kegan Paul, 1967, ch.2; and *The Study of Man*, Chicago University Press, 1959 and later editions, Lecture 2. Many thinkers from Plato at least have seen existence as a hierarchical structure, but Polanyi has given considerable attention to the epistemology of the relations between the levels.

23   L.G. Geering, *Tomorrow's God*, Wellington: Bridget Williams Books, 1994, pp.141-2.

24   Mary Hesse, *Science and the Human*

Imagination, London, SCM Press 1954, pp.15-16.

25 Idem, p.16.

26 An excellent summary account of the encouragement of work in the Judaeo-Christian tradition, and the abhorrence of manual labour among the Greeks, is found in H.P. Nebelsick, *Renaissance and Reformation*, Edinburgh, T.& T. Clark, 1992, pp. 177-84.

27 For a similar account, see R. Hooykaas, *Religion and the Rise of Modern Science*, Edinburgh, Scottish Academic Press, (1972), 1984, ch.4, on experimental science.

Chapter Six

1 See K.S. Latourette, *A History of Christianity*, London: Eyre and Spottiswoode, 1954, ch.10.

2 C. Dawson, *Religion and the Rise of Western Culture*, New York: Doubleday (1950) 1991, p.63.

3 Quoted by C. Dawson, op. cit., p.53.

4 There is little easily available on Bede as scientist, and my quotations and general information comes from C.B. Kaiser, op. cit., pp.24-25.

5 Kaiser, op. cit., p.44; his pp.42-51 survey the development of medicine in relation to religion through the mediaeval period.; Jaki, op.cit., pp.192-3.

6 Jaki, op. cit., pp.194-5.

7 C.A. Nallino, in J.Hastings (ed.) *Encyclopaedia of Religion and Ethics*, Edinburgh: T. & T. Clark, vol. 12, 1921, p.99. This 13-page article on Islam and the heavenly bodies is a mine of information.

8 S.L. Jaki, 'The Physics of Impetus and the Impetus of the Koran', a 1984 essay reprinted in his *The Absolute Beneath the Relative*, Lanham: University Press of America, 1988, p.150. The whole essay is highly relevant.

9 Idem, p.151.

10 Idem, p.150.

Chapter Seven

1 A.N. Whitehead, *Science in the Modern World*, Cambridge: The University Press, 1926, p.7, and ch.1, The Origins of Modern Science, *passim*.

2 M.B. Forster, 'The Christian Doctrine of Creation and the Rise of Modern Natural Science', *Mind* 43, 1934, pp.446-68; Christian Theology and Modern Science of *Nature*; 44, 1935, pp.439-66, and 45, 1936, pp.1-27.

3 C.B. Kaiser, op. cit., pp.89-90.

4 M. Clagett, *The Science of Mechanics in the Middle Ages*, Madison: University of Wisconsin Press 1961, p.536.

5 From N.Murphy's review of Margaret Wertheim's *Pythagoras' Trousers: God, Physics and the Gender Wars*, Times Books, in *Books and Culture*, Sept.-Oct. 1996, p.11.

6 On the persistence of Aristotelianism and the relevance of process theology and National Socialism, I am indebted to H.P. Nebelsick's chapter on the Reformation and the Rise of Science (especially p.160) in his *Renaissance and Reformation*. As recognized above, these historical issues are always complex and I have been following one main and basic strand; other more negative consequences of the 219 Paris condemnations are suggested in Jean Gimpel, *The Medieval Machine*, Penguin Books 1977, pp.182-5, 197-200.

Chapter Eight

1 An article bridging ancient and modern Gnosticisms and serving as a bridge to what is to come in the final chapter: Eric Osborn, Gnosticism: First Century Ideas Reappear to Contradict the Christian Message, *The Auburn Report* (Melbourne) 9(6), Dec. 1997, pp.4-7; philosophical structures and theological suppositions. [Available, like many others in this bibliography, in the ACCESS service of The DeepSight Trust]

2 L.G. Geering, *Tomorrow's God*, as cited, pp.187 for first two and p.115 for third quotation. He was the first Professor of Relgious Studies in the Victoria University of Wellington and previously Principal of the Presbyterian Theological College in Dunedin; he survived a trial for heresy in the 1960s and became the best known public figure expounding an allegedly front-line theology for over three decades. See my Consequences of a Basic Mistake, *Stimulus* (Masterton, N.Z.) 5(2), May 1997, pp.37-42, for my main critique.

3 Idem, p.115.

4 Idem, pp.115-6.

5 See Frances Young, *The Making of the Creeds*. London: S.C.M. Press 1991, p.93, and

pp.91-98; excellent on dualism in this period.

Chapter Nine

1   See my New Religious Movements in Primal Societies, in J.R. Hinnells (ed.), *A Handbook of Living Religions*. New York: Viking; Harmondsworth: Penguin Books, 1984, pp. 439-49, 454. Also 24 entries in *The Penguin Dictionary of Religions*, same editor and publishers. Also the six volumes (by continental area), *Bibliography of New Religious Movements in Primal Societies*, Boston: G.K. Hall, 1977-92, annotated.

2   See Bronwyn Elsmore, *Mana From Heaven: A Century of Maori Prophets in New Zealand*. Tauranga: Moana Press 1989; and her other writings.

3   See my *New Religious movements in Islamic West Africa, Islam and Christian Muslim Relations* (Selly Oak Colleges, Birmingham) 4(1), June 1993, pp.3-35.

4   See my The Relationship Between Development and New Religious Movements in Tribal Societies of the Third World, in F. Ferre and R.H. Mataragnon (eds.), *God and Global Justice; Religion and Poverty in an Unequal World*, New York: Paragon House 1985, pp.84-110.

Chapter Ten

1   See his *Tomorrow's God*, p.107.

2   First published in 1880, then in 12 volumes, 1907-15, and in various shorter forms since.

3   Susan Greenwood et al., Current Research on Paganism and Witchcraft in Britain, *Journal of Contemporary Religion*, 10(2), 1995, p.189.

4   Idem, p.189.

5   See several reports in *The Journal of Contemporary Religion*, 10(2), 1995.

6   Dr Stephen May of St. John's College, Auckland, illustrates another genre of escape from current culture in his theological study of science fiction, *Stardust and Ashes*, London: SPCK 1998. He refers, e.g., to Brian Aldiss' three-volume *Helliconia Trilogy* and to his Hothouse as built around a cyclic view of history and demolition of the myth of progress.

7   This comment deserves explanation. When I arrived back in New Zealand in 1989, I was disturbed at some of the courses in the humanities being offered by the University of Auckland Centre for Continuing Education, and also by their thrice-yearly Saturday all-day seminars offered year by year by Professor Geering. I knew that the University would close ranks against any critique from an apparent outsider, so I decided to offer a short course in 1991 on Michael Polanyi, to represent a different viewpoint. This surprisingly attracted 23 and was successful. In 1995 I decided to offer a one-day Saturday seminar on 'Science and Religion'. This was in the same mode as Professor Geering's still continuing series, and I indicated early in the seminar publicity statement for the Centre that I would be critiquing his position. The Centre tried unsuccessfully to shift me from the Saturday model to another kind of course, and apparently believed that it had banned criticism by one lecturer of any other lecturer! When its publicity appeared, my reference to Geering was demoted to the end and then bracketed as an aside. They also advertised the wrong seminar date! Shortly before the Saturday I was reprimanded for having arranged publicity in my own constituencies, and restored the reference to the Geering critique; it was wrongly assumed that I had undertaken not to critique what had apparently become the 'establishment'! Any such injunction would presumably be illegal by contradicting the law requiring the University to be the "critic and conscience of society." The seminar enrolled over 80, including the then President of the Royal Society of N.Z., to endure six hours on a heavy subject. This is a sample of the intolerance that marks Western postmodern culture, and not least in its universities. I should add that Lloyd Geering is an old and respected friend dating from my chaplaincy days when he was a student in the early 1940s, and this remains despite the polarity between our present views.

8   See M. Bowman, *Journal of Contemporary Religion* 10(2), 1995, pp.145-47. See also G.E. Veith Jr., The New Tribalism, in his *Postmodern Times*. Wheaton: Crossway, 1994, pp.153-6.

Chapter Eleven

1   L.G. Geering, *Tomorrow's God*, p. 169.

2   Idem, p.229.

3   2nd. edn. Chicago University Press, 1970; see also J. Polkinghorne, *One World*, London: SPCK, 1986, pp.12ff., and John Horgan, *The End of Science: Facing the Limits of Knowledge in the Twilight of the Scientific Age*. Reading, Mass.: Addison-Webley Pub., 1996.

4   See G.E. Veith, Jr., *Postmodern Society*, Wheaton: Crossway, 1994, p.182: "Hostile to science, many put their faith in 'alternative medicine', in natural foods and herbal medicine, Taoist acupuncture and Hindu meditation, all of which owe more to pre-modern paganism than to modern science. Medicine merges with psychology in 'holistic' therapies..."

5   S.L. Jaki, 'Science and Religion', in M. Eliade (gen. ed.) *Encyclopedia of Religion*, vol.13, p.132, referring to Capra's widely popular but cosmologically naive *The Tao of Physics* (Wildwood House, 1975).

6   Quoted in David Bosch, *Believing in the Future*. Trinity Press International, Valley Forge/Gracewing, Leominster, 1995, p.1, from Küng's Projekt Weltethos.

7   *As You Like It*, II, vii, 139.

8   J. Monod, *Chance and Necessity*. London: Collins/Fontana, 1974, p.160, as quoted by M. Midgley, op. cit., p.43.

9   *Tomorrow's God*, pp.235-6.

10 Jack Solomon, *The Signs of Our Time*. New York: Harper & Row, 1988, p.235.

11 Idem, p.236.

Chapter Twelve

1   H. Butterfield, *The Origins of Modern Science*, as cited, p.viii.

2   L.G. Geering, *God in the New World*, p.21.

3   L.G. Geering, in *Tomorrow's God*, tentatively on p.115, more emphatically as above on p.118, and with a range of scholars in support – C.F. von Weizacker, A.N. Whitehead, Peter Berger, Harvey Cox and Jacques Monod; none of them an historian of science or religion – these disciplines are conspicuously lacking from his sources.

4   I have dealt with the epistemological issue in my 'Polarized Polemics or Pooled Perspectives', *Stimulus* (Masterton, N.Z.) 1(1), Feb. 1993, pp.10-15; and with Polanyi's con-

tribution in *The Theological Significance of Michael Polanyi*, Idem, 5(1), Feb. 1997, pp.12-19.

5   See article 'Know' by J.-L. Leuba in J.J. von Allmen (ed.), *Vocabulary of the Bible*. London: Lutterworth, 1958, pp.221-3, which contrasts Greek and biblical epistemology.

6   From my 'Religion: Impediment or Saviour of Science?' in *Science and Education* (Dordrecht), 5, April 1996, pp. 155-6. See also T.F. Torrance, 'Theological and Scientific enquiry. Conjoint research between theology and science at their points of deepest convergence', *Journal of the American Scientific Affiliation*, 38(1), March 1986, pp.2-10.

7   See M.J. Bozack, 'Physics in the Theological Seminary', *Journal of the Evangelical Theological Society*, 36(1), March 1993, pp.65-76. Also C.B. Kaiser, 'Christology and Complementarity', *Religious Studies*, 12, 1976, pp. 37-48; and S.L. Jaki, 'Science and Christian Theism: a Mutual Witness', *Scottish Journal of Theology*, 32, 1979, p.569.

8   See full discussion of singularities in S.L. Jaki's Gifford Lectures, *The Road of Science and the Ways to God*, Edinburgh: Scottish Academic Press/Chicago University Press, 1978, ch.17, 'Cosmic Singularity'.

9   T.F. Torrance, *Preaching Christ Today*, Grand Rapids; Eerdmans, 1994, p.24.

10 See T.F. Torrance, 'The Church in the new era of scientific and sociological change', in *The Month*, 1973, 6(4), pp.136-42, and 6(6), pp.176-80; repr. in his *Theology in Reconciliation*. London: G. Chapman 1975, pp.267-93.

11 M. Polanyi, in *Nature*, vol.147, 25 Jan. 1941, p.119.

Provocative Postcript

1   Neil Broom, *How Blind Is The Watchmaker?*, Aldershot: Ashgate/Avebury, expected 1998.

2   In *The Ecologist*, 28(1), Jan.-Feb. 1998, pp.23-28; following quotation is from p.23. The aggressive thrust of the title and of the introductory paragraph derives more from the editor than the author.

3   Idem, p.28.

4   Idem, p.23.

The following works are suggested as a preliminary or background work:

CAHILL, Thomas. *The Gifts of the Jews. How a Tribe of Desert Nomads Changed the Way Everyone Thinks and Feels.* New York: Nan A. Talese/Doubleday, 1998, 291p. This arrived after the present text was finished; it is a scholarly but popular, beautifully written account of the basic cultural innovations of the Hebrews, especially re *time*, which gave the world *history*, and re the *individual* which lies behind *democracy*. His basic theme of time and history fills out our chapter 4, section on 'De-sacralized time'. He does not deal with science, which we have shown to develop *from* the Hebrews rather than *by* them. He does affirm, however, the magnitude of the Hebrew cultural revolution, which has only one of its contributions developed in our study of science.

BROOKE, J.H. *Science and Religion. Some Historical Perspectives.* Cambridge University Press 1991. Especially for its fine bibliographical essay, pp.348-403, which nevertheless omits some of the following sources.

BUTTERFIELD, Herbert. *The Origins of Modern Science 1300-1800.* London: G. Bell, 1949. Especially chs.1 (impetus), and 4 (downfall of Greek physics). Fairly popular, just as Cambridge University was preparing to teach history of science.

CLAGETT, M. *Greek Science in Antiquity.* New York: Abelard-Schuman 1955. Especially pp.130-45 on early Christian Fathers, and pp. 169-76 on Philoponus.

HESSE, Mary. *Science and the Human Imagination.* London: SCM, 1954. Especially ch.1, Mediaeval cosmology. Very readable, by a philosopher.

JAKI, S.L. *Science and Creation.* Edinburgh: Scottish Academic Press, rev. & enlarged ed. 1986. Covers cosmologies of 11 cultures and religions in erudite, historical detail. Simpler paperback version, *Cosmos and Creator*, less interesting. Same publisher, 1980.

JAKI, S.L. *Scientist and Catholic.* Front Royal, VA.; Christendom Press, 1991. Simpler account of Pierre Duhem than his big life, *Uneasy Genius*. Reprints 25 essays by Duhem; an invaluable source.

KAISER, C.B. *Creation and the History of Science.* Grand Rapids: Eerdmans, 1991. More detailed and scholarly.

LOUTH, Andrew. *Discerning the Mystery: an Essay on the Nature of Theology.* Oxford: Clarendon Press, 1983. Examines the division between theology and spirituality in our split culture, as background to our essay.

NEBELSICK, H.P. *Circles of God.* Edinburgh: Scottish Academic Press, 1985. Especially first 111 pp.; history of science and theology, simpler than Kaiser, includes Philoponus.

NEBELSICK, H.P. *The Renaissance, the Reformation and the Rise of Science.* Edinburgh: T.& T. Clark, 1992. Covers early period summarily, especially Christian critique of Aristotle.

NEBELSICK, H.P. *Theology and Science in Mutual Modification*. Belfast: Christian Journals 1981. More theological and on the modern period.

NEWBIGIN, Lesslie. *Foolishness to the Greeks. The Gospel and Western Culture*. Grand Rapids: Eerdmans, 1986. The most useful introduction to the cultural issue, with a good chapter 4, What can we know? The dialogue with science.

POLKINGHORNE, J. *One World. The Interaction of Science and Theology*. London: SPCK, 1986, 114p. Paperback on recent situation; not historical.

POLKINGHORNE, J. *Science and Creation*. London: SPCK 1988, 113p. Paperback. By a F.R.S., physicist and theologian.

SAMBURSKY, Sam. *The Physical World of Late Antiquity*. London: Routledge, 1962. Especially chapter, 'The Unity of Heaven and Earth', on Philoponus, and *passim*.

VON WEIZACKER, C.F. *The Relevance of Science*. London: Collins, 1964. Especially the long chapter on 'What is secularization?'. By a distinguished scientist.

WHITEHEAD, A.N. *Science and the Modern World*. Cambridge University Press, 1927. Especially the bombshell ch.1, Origins of Modern Science. A scientist-philosopher.

YOUNG, Frances. *The Making of the Creeds*. London: SCM 1991. Especially pp.91-98, her excellent, succinct account of the dualism issue and the Gnostics.

For further reflection and critique:

GAUCHET, Marcel. *The Disenchantment of the World. A Political History of Religion*. Trans. from the French, with Introduction by Canadian philosopher Charles Taylor, Princeton University Press, 1997, 228pp.

An atheist French political philosopher places religion at the centre of the human condition, and accordingly derives the Enlightenment and modernity from Christianity, as we similarly derive the associated movement of science. The classification of religions into 'primeval' (our tribal or primal), Axial and Christian (our Abrahamic, etc.) corresponds closely to our system. He also inverts the common league table of religions, so that the primals are described as the most fully formed religions.

The inclusion of Judaism with the Axials we can accept in terms of his first broad division, but not beyond this. In a sense he agrees when he presents Christianity as 'the religion for departing from religion' – i.e., for giving the proper autonomy to the created secular realm as we have done. It is this 'disenchantment of the world' which shows how the Enlightenment could develop only within the Christian sphere. Here the Incarnation confirmed the importance of the secular; it 'de-sacralized' all forms of human leadership and so made the secular state possible, and replaced concentration on the past with working for a future, which is the seed of modern science.

The above draws upon a long review by Brian C. Anderson in *First Things*, no.84, June-July 1998, pp.55-57; a copy is available from The DeepSight Trust *ACCESS* service, PO Box 87-362, Meadowbank, Auckland, New Zealand.

INDEX

Step-by-Step Guide
to the Historical Diagram

The following is intended as an easy-to-follow guide for what may at first appear a rather complex diagram on the Inside Back Cover. Marginal numbers are 'diagram-map' references, not an historical time scale.

A. Left Side: 1-2
The oval is the representative of the encapsulated, unitive cosmologies of tribal peoples and primal religions, where all is potentially sacralized, with sketch of its internal hierarchy, the macrocosm of the upper level as pattern for the microcosms of the lower levels. See p.24.

B. Top Half, Right Across: 3-12
3-4. Axial Religions and Greek philosophers' Dualism separating the Spiritual from the depreciated Material worlds, represented by circles overlapping in the present life (3), but destined to be separated when the Spiritual is freed (4). This is 'premodernity'.

5-7. Continuing Greek and popular Christian dualisms, through the Mediaeval period and 16th century, when 'modern science' begins with Descartes' dualism of the internal thinking mind and the outside material world. The mind and the outside world separating into the 'subjective' realms of religion, morals and values, and the 'objective' realm of science. This leads to a 'reversed dualism', with primacy for the material world known through science, and the worlds of religion, morals, and values losing the status of objective existence and permanency. This initiates the era of 'modernity'.

8. Subjective world absorbed into this world of scientific fact, as a mental creation to suit our changing historical or cultural needs. The dualist concept is not needed, since there is only this one world and the variations we can produce within it. This is the era of 'postmodernity'.

9-10. This is non-dualist 'Monism', which breaks up into many similar monistic worlds in a multi-cultural, relativist world society.

10-11. These in turn break up into sub-cultural monistic worlds, and further collapse into whatever 'world' each culture likes to create for its 'science', and each individual for a personal religion, ethic, values, lifestyle, etc.

11-12. Final collapse into a totally plural society with no common truth or values rooted in one shared, objective reality, i.e., into nihilism and anarchy.

C. Bottom Half, Right Across: 3-12

3. Hebrew tribes' de-sacralized world with integrated, open, contingent relation betwen the Creator and a creation which is appreciated: a duality cosmology.

4-9. Working out a doctrine of creation in relation to science, and in opposition to continuing dualisms, from the Early Christian Fathers to Philoponus, and through the mediaeval and modern science periods.

9-10. Nineteenth century beginnings of a non-dualist field-theory physics in Faraday, James Clerk Maxwell, and Einstein, in critique of Cartesianism.

10-12. Twentieth century non-dualist relational physics, in relativity and quantum theory.

Similar revolution in revival of trinitarian and relational theology. Abandonment of the subjectivity/objectivity dichotomy in theory of knowledge – K. Barth, M. Polanyi, etc.

2-11. New tribal religious movements from the 16th century following the Hebrew tribes into a duality cosmology, and not into Axial dualist worldviews, as did tribes in antiquity.